EUTHANASIA

DAVID ALTON with MARTIN FOLEY

EUTHANASIA

Getting to the heart
of the matter

ST PAULS

Also in this series:
By David Alton with Martin Foley
Abortion – Getting to the heart of the matter

Also by David Alton:
Pilgrim Ways – Catholic Pilgrimage Sites in Britain and Ireland

ST PAULS Publishing
187 Battersea Bridge Road, London SW11 3AS, UK
www.stpauls.ie

Copyright © ST PAULS, 2005
ISBN 085439 692 6

Set by TuKan DTP, Fareham, UK
Printed by Progress Press Company Limited, Valletta, Malta

ST PAULS is an activity of the priests and brothers
of the Society of St Paul who proclaim the Gospel
through the media of social communication

Contents

Introduction   7

What is wrong with euthanasia?   21

The Parliamentary battle   45

Tony Bland and Anthony Devine –
   despair and hope   67

'Our lives are worth living!'   89

Conclusion   101

Appendix   107

Introduction

The Archbishop of Canterbury, Dr Rowan Williams, says that euthanasia is 'an act of violence, an attempt to take possession of the future... even if euthanasia were legalised in some form and pragmatic anxieties overcome, it could not be a course of action endorsed by Christians.' This is a view shared by the Chief Rabbi, Dr Jonathan Sacks, by Roman Catholics, by Muslims and, indeed, by many people with no religious belief. The medical profession remains overwhelmingly opposed.

Yet, a relentless campaign, highly sophisticated and deeply manipulative, is being waged in the UK to alter our traditional beliefs and to change our laws. Be under no illusion, if this happens, our care homes and hospices – the sanctuaries that have traditionally overseen the care of the elderly, the sick and the dying – will become charnel houses. In seeking to 'take possession of the future' we will demand of our doctors that they become licensed killers. The collateral effects on society's attitudes are incalculable.

The issue for Christians is not simply about whether euthanasia should be endorsed, it is about whether something so fundamental should occur with barely a murmur of protest. Thirty years ago Christian quietism – and a docile, false belief that abortion would never be legalised – paved the way for a law that has claimed six million lives. With what indifference will we now allow the fate of the unborn to be visited on the sick and dying?

To those who say, 'it couldn't happen here' we need look no further than neighbouring countries such as Holland and Belgium. In Holland it began when a blind eye was turned to so called 'mercy killing'. Then the law was altered to provide those doing the killing with some protection. This they called 'voluntary eutha-nasia'. Then they said relatives and friends should be able to determine a sick person's 'best interests' and voluntary euthanasia for all over the age of twelve was quickly followed by involuntary euthanasia. Early in 2005 a Dutch medical journal revealed that at Gröningen Hospital doctors had killed twenty-two babies with spina bifida. They had made their actions public so that the law might be further changed enabling it to apply from birth. Before Britain moves onto this same slippery slope we need to take a deep look at the cesspit into which we will rapidly descend.

Throughout the last decade public opinion has been assiduously prepared for such a change of law. It is no coincidence that Baroness Warnock, the elite's favourite philosopher, has been opining that 'Maybe it has come down to saying, okay, they can stay alive, but the family will have to pay for it. Otherwise, it will be an awful drain on public resources.' She went on to add 'I don't see why the rest of us should be sacrificed to the scruples of the medical profession.'

The Prime Minister, Mr Blair, has trenchantly stated that 'we will not in any shape or form countenance the deliberate killing of people.' He added that 'I would have thought that that position would recommend itself to everyone.' Clearly not to Baroness Warnock, Lord Joffe or their supporters in the Voluntary Euthanasia Society who have been driving on this debate.

Lady Warnock's argument about economics is deeply utilitarian but it is one which will doubtless commend itself to health service managers looking to make budget savings. The sick are being conditioned to believe that it is their duty to die. Having established the right to die, it rapidly becomes a duty to die. Sick and disabled people are being made to believe that they are a burden on society or their relatives. In constantly emphasising blocked hospital beds and waiting lists, vulnerable people – many of them acutely depressed already – will feel they owe it to their relatives and to society to seek a lethal injection.

In this climate, doctors will then stop bothering to report what they are doing. That again is what has happened in Holland. At a parliamentary meeting organised by the Voluntary Euthanasia Society, Professor John Griffiths of the Faculty of Law, University of Gröningen, said that only 50–60 per cent of cases of euthanasia in the Netherlands are reported to the proper authorities. More worryingly still, Professor Griffiths admitted that it is the 'more problematic' cases that are escaping the control system. In other words, it is impossible to establish an effective regulatory framework for assisted suicide and euthanasia. It is blatantly obvious who has most to fear from these attempts to change attitudes and law.

The Disability Rights Commission say: 'Until we are convinced that sufficient regulation and safeguards can, and will be, put in place to ensure the right to life of disabled people, we will not support the legalisation of assisted suicide and voluntary euthanasia.' Help the Aged say: 'This (Lord Joffe's Patient (Assisted Dying) Bill) is not a Bill that Help the Aged would support, because we do not support changes to the law relating to euthanasia.'

A few months ago, at a meeting in Parliament, which I chaired, we were addressed by four medics who explained why they believe Dutch-style euthanasia laws would be a disaster for Britain.

Dr Nigel Sykes, the Medical Director of St Christopher's Hospice in London, agreed that there is sympathy for euthanasia among the general public. 'However' he said, 'patients themselves usually do not want euthanasia.' Only 15–20 per cent of cancer patients want euthanasia and only 3.5 per cent of patients dying of cancer want euthanasia. 'Euthanasia is a minority interest amongst the terminally ill. It is only those who are healthy who want Lord Joffe's Bill.'

In a recent opinion poll of medics the majority of UK doctors who responded opposed euthanasia and more than three quarters said that they would not be prepared to carry it out even if it were made legal. Not one single doctor working in palliative care who was polled was in favour of euthanasia.

11

Some people think that so-called doctor-assisted dying is different from euthanasia. The moment you try to define legally phrases such as what is meant by 'suffering unbearably' and what is a 'serious and progressive physical illness', you can see that there is no practical difference between doctor-assisted dying and euthanasia. It is just playing with words. Advanced or perhaps even not-so-advanced rheumatoid arthritis and diabetes would fall under the definition of 'serious physical illnesses' and euthanasia would become a 'symptom-control choice', one option of 'treatment' among others. Having watched my own mother die of crippling arthritis I am not unaware of the loss of dignity and the suffering of serious illness. But I also know what would have been lost if I had commissioned her premature death or if she had been encouraged to believe that her life was worthless and that she would have been better off dead. As the doctors who spoke in Parliament stated, it will be nigh impossible for a doctor to ascertain whether a patient is suffering 'unbearably'. In those circumstances we should not confuse care and kill – they can never be used as synonyms.

Then there is the question of competency. A patient who is in pain or is confused would not be considered competent to consent to an assisted death. However, if society endorses euthanasia as an 'appropriate treatment choice' for competent patients, surely it will be only a matter of time until euthanasia will be offered as appropriate 'treatment' to patients that are temporarily or permanently incompetent. Not everything in life can be reduced to a matter of apparent choice. Choices always carry consequences.

How are we to ensure that consent to euthanasia is given by free and informed choice? Experience in Oregon, USA – where physician-assisted suicide has been legalised – illustrates that the longer euthanasia has been legal, the higher the percentage of patients who think that they have become a burden to society and should be requesting euthanasia. The right becomes a duty.

When a member of the House of Lords, Lord Joel Joffe, first introduced his euthanasia Bill (the Patient (Assisted Dying Bill – of which I will say more later in the book) it did not even allow for conscientious objection by doctors who refuse to take part in euthanasia. This, too, illustrates the relentless agenda of those seeking to change our laws. They cannot apparently cope with the idea that a medic might not find it acceptable to kill their patient. The entire medical profession will thus be subverted. Peer pressure within medical practices and pressure in medical schools – even affecting student applications – will ensure that anyone who tries to exercise their conscience will be passed over for promotion or completely excluded in the first place. What is made permissible rapidly becomes normative and in due course will become compulsory.

There is also the real concern that because killing is cheaper than caring, killing will become a frequently used 'treatment'. The doctors told parliamentarians that they could envisage a situation where people, not just old people, would feel that they have to pass an 'MOT' and if they fail, they will be 'bumped off'.

Tellingly, Dr Sykes asked why pain relief has been introduced into the argument about euthanasia. Pain relief is part and parcel of every-day medicine. We do not need a new Act of Parliament for doctors and nurses to provide pain relief for their patients – but the implication is that anyone who opposes euthanasia and doctor-assisted dying is somehow in favour of pain or suffering. Dr Sykes said attempts to change the law would have 'disastrous effects'.

During the same meeting we heard from Dr Peter Hildering who is President of the Netherlands Physicians League. He shared a case history: a sixty-five-year-old Dutch woman, opposed to euthanasia for religious reasons, who had been diagnosed with cancer. When euthanasia was initially discussed, she refused. As the disease progressed she saw herself becoming a burden to her husband and asked her GP to help her die so that she would not be a burden to her husband anymore. Legalising euthanasia encourages people to believe that everyone will be better off when they are dead. Revealingly, Dr Hildering said that there are Dutch patients who now go to Germany for treatment since they are afraid that they might be killed in the Netherlands against their will.

Today, euthanasia is used in cases where the wait for treatment is too long. In the Netherlands it is only in the last three years that there has been any significant expansion of hospice care. Euthanasia has damaged the doctor-patient relationship by giving doctors the permission to kill and, inevitably, in changing our attitude towards the sick, the elderly, or terminally ill, it damages society. Good palliative care cannot be associated with euthanasia – and mercifully, in Britain, where we have such a developed hospice movement we do not need to legalise the killing of patients. Lord Walton of Detchant, who chaired the House of Lords Select Committee, which in 1994 came out against euthanasia, says that our provision of palliative care makes euthanasia unnecessary. Indeed, its provision would probably destroy the hospice movement.

Legalisation would also make time of death become a matter of social engineering. The slippery slope is real. Dr Hildering told parliamentarians that people in Holland are being killed who do not want to be killed. He said that transparency is impossible: 'One can either open the door to euthanasia or keep it shut. There is no middle ground. If you open the door a little, soon it will be wide open.' This was Dr Hildering's sobering conclusion.

Professor Tim Maughan, Director of the Wales Cancer Trials Network at Cardiff University, also spoke passionately at our meeting against euthanasia. He said that there are two groups of patients that would be placed at high risk if euthanasia were legalised: first, patients with cancer or an otherwise serious disease including patients who experience serious depression at the time of diagnosis. Those patients may request euthanasia at the time of diagnosis, however that request frequently evaporates and the request is later regretted. Depression is a major predictor for euthanasia requests. Second, patients who feel that they are a burden to others and to the NHS. They want to live but they *feel* themselves to be a burden.

Professor Maughan said we need to ask some searching questions. Who would a change in law be seeking to help? The dying or their relatives? Is it right to enable a few patients to die while at the same time putting a large number of patients at risk? What would the effect of legalised euthanasia be on the thinking and morale of NHS staff? Professor Maughan pointed out that doctors in the Netherlands now want to do away with all the regulatory structure surrounding euthanasia. They are becoming weary of having to report what it is that they do.

He also nailed the idea constantly trumpeted by the Voluntary Euthanasia Society that morphine is regularly being used in terminal care to shorten life. In other words, that we sanction euthanasia by default. This is 'nonsense' he said. Morphine is being used to treat symptoms. Patients are dying of the underlying disease. Professor Maughan's conclusion was that euthanasia 'would lead to widespread abuse' increasing the risk to the most vulnerable members of society.

During that same meeting parliamentarians also heard from Dr Robert Twycross, Emeritus Clinical Reader in Palliative Medicine, Oxford

University. He insisted that 'euthanasia must never become part of normal medical practice' and that 'society must safeguard the right to life'. Dr Twycross was in no doubt that 'if we kill voluntarily we will eventually offer involuntary euthanasia.'

So no one should claim that they were not warned. Pope John Paul II has been quite clear about the threat. In his 1995 encyclical *Evangelium Vitae* (the Gospel of Life) he identified one of the more alarming features of the 'culture of death' we live in – an

> excessive preoccupation with efficiency... which sees the growing number of elderly and disabled people as intolerable and too burdensome. These people are very often isolated by their families and by society, which are organised almost exclusively on the basis of criteria of productive efficiency, according to which a hopelessly impaired life no longer has any value.[1]

As a man who visibly struggled with old age and infirmity, and offered inspiration and hope to many others in a similar condition, his response to this threat was a constant plea for solidarity with the old, the weak and the terminally ill.

The risks of legalising euthanasia are obvious.

Only by rousing the conscience of this nation and only through the effective lobbying of parliamentarians will we see this threat defeated. This short book is a modest contribution to informing public opinion of the danger we face.

NOTES

1 *Evangelium Vitae* (March 1995, para 64); http://www.vatican.va/edocs/ENG0141/_INDEX.HTM

What is wrong with euthanasia?

We live in an increasingly secular age in which the rights of the individual, in particular the freedom to make autonomous choices, are seen as paramount. Conversely, the principles and prohibitions contained within the Judaeo Christian tradition are viewed as outdated and in need of reinterpretation so that they can more easily accord with our contemporary outlook. It is in this context that the debate surrounding voluntary euthanasia persists. Euthanasia is defined as 'the painless killing of a patient suffering from an incurable disease or in an irreversible coma',[1] and is derived from the Greek 'well death'. What distinguishes voluntary euthanasia from the other forms of euthanasia, non-voluntary and involuntary, is that the killing takes place with the expressed consent of the patient.

Provided that the patient's consent is freely given and informed, voluntary euthanasia may well appear as beneficent for the patient and its consequences harmless for wider society. However, that it remains illegal in the United Kingdom and continues to provoke fierce moral debate is due to the fact that it contravenes the prohibition on killing derived from our Judaeo Christian tradition[2], a prohibition which permeates throughout society's moral and legal fabric. As Pope John Paul II declared in his encyclical, *Evangelium Vitae* – the Gospel of Life, 'euthanasia must be called a false mercy, and indeed a disturbing "perversion" of mercy. True "compassion" leads to sharing another's pain; it does not kill the person whose suffering we cannot bear.'[3]

In contrast with this belief, the pressure to legalise voluntary euthanasia persists, its denial being seen as doing little to further the interests of individuals living together in a society.[4] As one observer put it: 'How can one explain to the agnostic yuppie that one should live out the last few weeks or months of a death from cancer complicated by multiple metastases and multiple organ difficulties?'[5]

Both its proponents and opponents recognise that if the case for voluntary euthanasia cannot be made out, then it is unlikely that the case can be made out for euthanasia of any sort.[6]

Recognising this, I would like in this chapter to advance the philosophical case against voluntary euthanasia, to demonstrate that it is not ethically justifiable. The central tenet of my argument is that it is ordinarily wrong to kill human beings, even with their consent. The much vaunted counter claim based on autonomy is fallacious and collapses into arbitrary quality of life considerations. Furthermore, though much derided, the traditional or orthodox position[7] on euthanasia and the treatment of the terminally ill, with its emphasis on the sanctity or inviolability of human life which Pope John Paul II did so much to proclaim,[8] can be rationally defended and shown to be in the best interests of patients and society as a whole.

It is widely acknowledged that '[R]ules in our moral code against actively causing the death of another person are not isolated fragments. They are threads in a fabric of rules that support respect for human life. The more threads we remove, the weaker the fabric becomes.'[9] We must therefore proceed with extreme caution in any weakening or unpicking of the prohibition against unjustified killing if 'the principle of the unconditional protection of innocent human life'[10] is to remain at the centre of our morality. Sadly, however, killing is coming to be seen as the 'ultimate medicine',[11] which, most definitely, it is not.

As human beings we all share a common humanity. Professor John Finnis identifies this as essentially a 'radical capacity for participating in the manner of a person – intelligently and freely – in human goods'.[12] These goods include knowledge, friendship, work and play. Yet the ultimate human good is life itself, as this good makes enjoyment of all the other goods possible. To lose your life is to lose all these goods, effectively one loses 'one's very reality as a human being'.[13] The reverse, however, does not apply. To lose the capacity for participating in one or more of the human goods, such as the capacity to think, is to lose an ability, not one's life. So long as life itself is present, the human person remains, albeit one may be an 'immature or damaged human person'.[14]

Thus, there is a wholeness to our human nature, not a dualistic account of a biological life and a biographical life with the latter taking precedence over the former.[15] Pope John Paul II has written that 'It is impossible to further the common good without acknowledging and defending the right to life, upon which all the other inalienable rights of individuals are founded and from which they develop.'[16] Human beings share equally an intrinsic dignity and value by virtue of our shared humanity. While some human goods may be instrumental to our flourishing as human beings, the most fundamental good, life itself, is intrinsic.[17] Consequently, '[I]n sustaining human bodily life, in however impaired a condition, one is sustaining the person whose life it is. In refusing to choose to violate it, one respects the person in the most fundamental and indispensable way.'[18] It is in this context that I refer to the prohibition on the killing of innocent human beings as being at the centre of morality, providing the cornerstone of whatever rights an individual may have. Our status as subjects of justice is not acquired and is not transient.

This brief account of the wrongness of killing and hence the wrongness of voluntary euthanasia can be elucidated and reinforced by an analysis of four distinct arguments in favour of voluntary euthanasia posited by Professor Peter Singer, an internationally renowned advocate for euthanasia.[19]

Singer begins by proposing four grounds for the wrongness of killing. The first is a utilitarian objection, that since self-conscious beings are capable of fearing their own death, killing them has worse effects on others.[20] Yet, as Singer correctly identifies, this reason against killing provides an extremely weak prohibition on voluntary euthanasia as the crux of voluntary euthanasia is that it takes place with the consent of the patient. Those who do not want to be killed need not consent and need not fear an untimely death. Singer's second ground is also utilitarian, that killing thwarts the victim's preference to go on living.[21] Again, this is a weak prohibition on voluntary euthanasia because the 'victim's' preference could equally be for death and if preferences to live or die are omnipotent, as Singer and others would hold,[22] then such a preference must be respected. This is not to say I endorse such a preference of utilitarian calculation. If our principles and ethics were to be guided by such a calculation then this could lead to the calamitous conclusion that one individual's preference to live can be outweighed by the combined preferences of others that he should die. Involuntary euthanasia then becomes a distinct possibility.

Singer's third ground for the wrongness of killing derives from his theory of rights. Whereas those of us who uphold the sanctity of life hold that there is a right to life which protects that fundamental good and is attached unconditionally to all innocent human beings, Singer believes that 'to have a right one must have the ability to desire that to which one has a right, so that to have a right to life one must be able to desire one's own continued existence.'[23] Consequently to kill a self-conscious being who desires to live is to violate their right to life, regardless of the quality of life or its prospects.[24] In this way the sanctity of life should be understood as protecting biographical, not biological lives.[25] Thus, where this individual wishes to die and has expressed that wish, there can be no objection to voluntary euthanasia as a competent individual is free to waive his right to life[26] and request that it be ended. To respect such a request 'is the very opposite of indifference to life. The respect for human life leads to a respect for human death.'[27]

Singer draws the analogy with a right to privacy which all human beings have.[28] Of course, one can waive such a right but one cannot alienate permanently one's right to privacy in general. Similarly, though one can give away property, one cannot alienate one's right to own property in general. However, should the right to life be waived nothing is left – once dead you can hardly retain a right to life in general! Such rights, including the right to life, attach unconditionally to all human beings and by their very nature are inalienable.[29] Thus, the analogy of waiving the right to life with waiving privacy rights or property rights is disingenuous and some further justification must be found for voluntary euthanasia by its supporters.

The most plausible justification for voluntary euthanasia is derivative from a rights based analysis. Singer's fourth ground for the wrongness of killing is '[R]espect for the autonomous decisions of rational agents.'[30] Again Singer identifies that this argument cuts both ways. While it prohibits the unjust killing of autonomous individuals, it also provides a purported justification of voluntary euthanasia in that 'if rational agents should autonomously choose to die, then respect for autonomy will lead us to assist them to do as they choose.'[31] This appeal to respect autonomy is put most forcefully by Professor Ronald Dworkin, another academic cheerleader for the pro-euthanasia lobby. (I am often struck by the number of armchair academics who support euthanasia in contrast to the doctors and nurses on the front-line who are largely opposed to the practice.) 'Making someone die in a way others approve, but he believes contradicts his own dignity, is a serious, unjustified, unnecessary form of tyranny.'[32]

Where our concern for an individual's welfare and respect for moral norms is incompatible with respect for that individual's wishes, the latter must take precedence.

However, the concept of autonomy, in particular the right to refuse medical treatment, is designed 'not to give persons a right to decide whether to live or die but to protect them from the unwanted interferences of others'.[33] The concept is rooted in the notion of the intrinsic value and dignity of the human person and thus can be overridden when autonomy is exercised in ways which contravene this notion and/or place other members of society at risk of harm.[34]

Professor Finnis correctly identifies two 'philosophically and morally erroneous judgements' inherent in the voluntary request to be killed.[35] The first is that in certain circumstances human life has no intrinsic value or dignity. Such a conclusion can only be maintained if an erroneous concept of the dualistic nature of human life is held, a concept I rebutted earlier. Furthermore, it is laden with arbitrary quality of life considerations which I will discuss shortly. The second false judgement is that the world would be a better place without the individual concerned. Such a conclusion demonstrates the dangers of exclusively utilitarian calculations where the individual loses sight of their own worth in amongst what are perceived as the stronger claims and preferences of other members of society.

The question also arises as to whether or not a person suffering from an incurable, terminal illness and in great pain can ever express a free choice to be killed. 'Pain does different things to different people'[36] and we need to be extremely wary of paying undue deference to 'statements that reflect mental illness, not free choice'.[37]

Nevertheless, the truly autonomous request for euthanasia cannot be discounted. I have defended what might be seen as a paternalist position yet even the proponents of unbridled autonomy recognise its limits. Singer appears to defend the prevention of people from becoming heroin addicts as 'justifiable paternalism'[38] yet when an individual's very life is at stake, he discounts the prohibition of voluntary euthanasia. For him, there are good reasons for voluntary euthanasia (pain and suffering) which do not extend to taking heroin. Yet if respect for autonomy is so important, reasons should not matter. That they do demonstrates that the appeal to autonomy is misleading and that the argument for voluntary euthanasia boils down to subjective and arbitrary 'Quality of life'[39] judgements.[40]

'Living is not the good, but living well. The wise man therefore lives as long as he should,

30

not as long as he can... He will always think of life in terms of quality, not quantity.'[41]

This statement encapsulates the rationale inherent in moves to legalise voluntary euthanasia. There is a denial of the fundamental good of life itself and a judgement that people should instinctively know when it is time to die (and, if need be, be reminded by their peers!). We are supposed to recognise that certain lives are not worth living, that they demean a patient's dignity and should be terminated. The late Professor Jim Rachels, who wrote extensively on euthanasia exemplifies this attitude. He dismisses the idea of the equal worth of human lives, '...the idea that some lives are more valuable than others is already a part of our common moral sense, it is not some insidious new thought which, once admitted will corrupt our hearts and lead us into unimaginable wickedness.'[42] To fail to recognise this is 'nothing but rhetorical bullying'.[43] Similarly, maintaining this quality of life ethic, Professor Dworkin argues that resources should not be wasted on 'damaged' individuals when there are others with conscious lives to lead.[44] Failure to recognise a right to die insults the idea of the sanctity of life.[45]

I cannot disagree strongly enough with Professors Rachels and Dworkin. The promotion of the idea that life can be of negative value is insidious and our failure to recognise the equal value of all human lives demonstrates a need to re-evaluate our common moral sense, rather than accede to individuals' mistaken requests to be killed. The fundamental good of life itself is too often overlooked and attention focuses on whether the patient's life is worthwhile, rather than whether treatment is worthwhile.[46]

Arguments in favour of voluntary euthanasia rest upon subjective and arbitrary quality of life judgements and can be countered by recapturing the notion of the intrinsic dignity and value of life itself and the immorality of acts of unjustified killing which extinguish this basic good. This position is frequently attacked as hypocritical in that it supports a variety of courses of action which result in the deaths of individuals yet condemns acts of voluntary euthanasia where the end result is the same. For example, Professor Rachels frequently criticised the widely drawn distinction between killing and letting die:

> The difference between killing and letting die does not, in itself, make a difference from the point of view of morality. If a doctor lets a patient die, for humane reasons, he is in the same moral position as if he had given the

patient a lethal injection for humane reasons.[47]

Where the patient is in severe pain, voluntary euthanasia can be construed 'as morally laudatory, if not obligatory'.[48]

Professor Rachels is right, to an extent, but the attempt to label the traditional or orthodox position as hypocritical is facile and mischievous. Killing and letting die (or selective non-treatment) are indistinguishable where the health care professional's *intention* is that the patient should die. Intention is the crucial element and in this context of voluntary euthanasia I acknowledge the freedom of patients who are incurably ill to refuse interventions that prolong dying and the freedom of physicians to honour such wishes provided the motivation is not suicidal or to assist in suicide. The sanctity of life doctrine is not vitalistic. A moral distinction is drawn 'between acts that permit death and acts that cause death'.[49]

Professor Rachels rejects such distinctions, his focus is solely on results and intention is only relevant to an assessment of the character of the agent.[50] He argues, '[O]nce the irrelevant considerations have been set aside, we will simply ask what is best for the patient.'[51] Nevertheless, intention is crucial as it concerns purpose.[52] 'If we draw out of an act all the motivating intention, the residue seems not to be the same act, if it is precisely speaking, any act at all.'[53]

The traditional or orthodox position thereby acknowledges that there can be a point to the cessation of life-prolonging treatment other than a desire to bring about the patient's death. The attempt to identify a competent refusal of treatment with voluntary euthanasia in all circumstances is misleading but is a tactic regularly employed by the pro-euthanasia lobby to sow seeds of confusion within people's minds.[54] The distinction between intention and foresight remains valid, but this does not mean to say that where an individual performs an act foreseeing a certain result, rather than intending it, he avoids responsibility altogether.[55] Though derided as 'a piece of complete sophistry'[56] the principle of double effect remains valid and applicable. However, all four elements of the principle must be satisfied for it to be properly applied.[57] To reject the distinction between the intended and the unintended would treat ends 'as potentially justifying any and every type of means'[58] with possibly dire consequences. Retaining such a distinction is consistent with the prohibition of voluntary euthanasia, whether by act or malevolent omission and does not entail the prolonging of life at all costs.

Coexistent with, and complimentary to, this distinction is the 'connection between what we are obliged to do and what we can do: our duties cannot extend beyond our physical and mental capacities.'[59] This distinction between ordinary and extraordinary treatments[60] allows the competent patient to reject extraordinary treatment, that which is significantly burdensome, futile or dangerous to the patient or others. Such a refusal need not be suicidal in intent, whereas the refusal of ordinary treatment, that is consisting of 'normal everyday means of sustenance',[61] can be seen as little other than suicidal.

This distinction has also been attacked as 'vague and morally unacceptable'[62] and as introducing the covert and repugnant quality of life judgements[63] which I have previously denounced. Yet, being rooted in exclusively medical indicators it does nothing of the sort. The refusal of treatment on the grounds that it is futile does not mean that the treatment would fail to restore a decent quality of life but, rather, that it would fail to achieve its proper function. The following example offers a useful analogy:

The use of a respirator to sustain a patient through a severe bout with a respiratory disease would be considered ordinary (it is clearly not futile); its use to sustain the life of a severely brain-damaged person in an irreversible coma would be considered extraordinary.[64]

The intention/foresight distinction, complemented by the ordinary/extraordinary distinction demonstrates that the prohibition on voluntary euthanasia can be maintained within a compassionate and caring environment. Nobody is considered 'better off dead' or judged to have a life 'not worth living'; rather the competent patient has scope to refuse treatment and doctors have a similar scope to withdraw treatment. Being founded largely on quality of life considerations, voluntary euthanasia crosses a moral rubicon which will inevitably lead to non-voluntary and possibly involuntary euthanasia.

Such an appeal to 'slippery slopes' is often made by those who have failed to overcome the case being presented.[65] Yet having demonstrated that voluntary euthanasia is not morally justifiable, brief reference needs to be made to the consequences which would flow from the legalisation of voluntary euthanasia. Physicians – let alone health service economists – may come to view those patients who have not expressed a request to be killed but are in a similar position to those who have as somehow deserving of death, or at least less of a priority for comprehensive treatment – the 'right to die' becomes the 'obligation to die'.[66] Once we start considering the worthwhileness of a patient's life then the lazy, feckless and unhealthy should be worried. Professor John Harris from the University of Manchester, who has in the past endorsed infanticide, acknowledges that '[N]on voluntary and involuntary euthanasia of persons is always wrong'[67] but such a statement can only be understood in its subtle definition of 'persons' which would, as far as people like Professors Harris and Singer are concerned, exclude the comatose, permanently unconscious and other immature or damaged individuals. Once it is accepted that certain competent persons can request death by active intervention or malevolent omission, then those with a comparatively worse medical prognosis or quality of life are ripe for premature death.

Furthermore, even those who in theory support voluntary euthanasia recoil from its practical application or legalisation on the basis that effective regulation would be impossible.[68] Being such a final act with no redress for the 'victim', regulation would have to be overwhelmingly stringent and proposals such as those outlined by Professor Rachels[69] inspire little confidence when the morality/lawfulness of an act of voluntary euthanasia will be decided after the event. As

Maguire identifies, '[T]he ways in which relatives and/or medical personnel could suction the desire to live out of a patient are not easily warded off by legislation.'[70] As I will go on to discuss in later chapters, studies of voluntary euthanasia in the Netherlands[71] represent a salutary reminder of the dangers of the practice and have led the editor of the *Journal of Medical Ethics* to observe that 'restrictions on euthanasia that legal controls in the Netherlands were supposed to have implemented are being extensively ignored and… it is surely justifiable to conclude… that the practice of euthanasia in the Netherlands is in poor control.'[72] The disastrous result of this lack of effective control has been the practice of non-voluntary and involuntary euthanasia in addition to the lawful practice of voluntary euthanasia.

To conclude, voluntary euthanasia can never be morally justifiable. Principles prohibiting unjustified killing, whether by act or malevolent omission lie at the core of morality. Such killing deprives an individual of the fundamental human good of life itself, the good that makes experience of all the other human goods possible and which remains, notwithstanding that the capacity to experience these other goods is permanently damaged, destroyed or is immature. This is what I mean when I refer to the intrinsic value of life.

The intrinsic value of life has been compared by one commentator to that of a beautiful work of art. Though the work of art may lose its instrumental value in the eyes of its owner, it retains its intrinsic value such that it would be wrong for the owner to destroy it.[73] Similarly, life remains precious, even though its instrumental value has diminished.

The onus lies upon those who seek to dilute principles prohibiting unjustified killing through the introduction of voluntary euthanasia. The crux of their argument, respect for autonomy, is specious. Their unwillingness to extend respect for autonomy beyond the terminally and incurably ill demonstrates that its limits are recognised. Properly exercised, autonomy should be consistent with the human goods, in particular, life itself. Essentially, the case for voluntary euthanasia collapses into quality of life judgements, which, by their very nature are selective and arbitrary and form a fragile basis for legalised killing. Increasingly, effective pain management, combined with upholding a traditional framework of ethics which draws logical distinctions between intention and foresight and ordinary and extra-ordinary means of treatment, allow the terminally and incurably ill to be treated in a compassionate manner. There may be difficult cases where pain relief may not be possible but killing patients in such circumstances should not be countenanced. 'Suffering people need the support of others; suffering people should not be encouraged to commit suicide by their community, or that community ceases to be a true community.'[74]

Finally, Professor Harris claims that 'the real problem of euthanasia is the tragedy of the premature and unwanted deaths of the thousands of people in every society who die for want of medical and other resources or who are allowed to die or are killed because others believe their lives are not worth sustaining.'[75] The argument runs that because resources are finite some people should be allowed to go to the wall: they should be conditioned to believe that their earliest possible death is for the greater good, and others might then live. A moral prohibition of voluntary euthanasia incorporates an absolute rejection of the notion that certain lives are not worth living while asserting that the intrinsic dignity and value of life can only truly be respected if increased resources are devoted to the care of individuals in *all* societies, in particular to palliative medicine.

NOTES

1 *Concise Oxford English Dictionary,* 10th Edition.

2 see Exodus Ch.20:13 (*New Testament Bible – Reader's Edition*).

3 *Evangelium Vitae* (1995, para. 66);
http://www.vatican.va/holy_father/john_paul_ii/encyclicals/
documents/hf_jp-ii_enc_25031995_evangelium-vitae_en.html

4 Tooley, M, *Killing & Letting Die* [2nd Edition], 'An Irrelevant
Consideration: Killing Versus Letting Die' in Steinbock, B, &
Norcross, A (eds.), (New York: Fordham University Press, 1994)
p.109.

5 Engelhardt Jr, H.T., *The Foundation of Bioethics* [2nd Edition],
(New York: OUP, 1996) p.353.

6 Singer, P, *Practical Ethics* [2nd Edition] (Cambridge: Cambridge
University Press, 1993) p.196; Oderberg, D.S., *Applied Ethics, A
Non-Consequentialist Approach* (Oxford: Blackwell Publishers,
2000) p.151.

7 Perhaps such a position could be more accurately defined as
'radical'.

8 Keown, J., 'Restoring Moral and Intellectual Shape to the Law
After Bland', *L.Q.R.* **113** (1997) 482-483.

9 Beauchamp, T.L. & Childress, J.F., *Principles of Biomedical Ethics*
[4th Edition], (New York: OUP, 1994) p.230.

10 Oderberg, D.S., *op. cit.,* p.48; see also Murphy, J.G., 'Is Killing
the Innocent Absolutely Immoral?' in Steinbock & Norcross,
Killing & Letting Die, op. cit., pp. 197-209.

11 Oderberg, D.S., *op. cit.,* p.70.

12 Finnis, J.M., 'A philosophical case against euthanasia' in Keown,
J, (ed.) *Euthanasia Examined – Ethical, clinical and legal perspectives*
(Cambridge: Cambridge University Press, 1995) p.31.

13 *Ibid.*

14 *Ibid.*

15 see Rachels, J., *The End of Life – Euthanasia & Morality* (Oxford:
OUP, 1986) p.5 & p.26 in particular.

16 *Evangelium Vitae* (1995, para. 101);
    http://www.vatican.va/holy_father/john_paul_ii/encyclicals/
    documents/hf_jp-ii_enc_25031995_evangelium-vitae_en.html

17 Finnis, J.M., 'Bland: Crossing the Rubicon?', *L.Q.R.* **109** (1993)
    334.

18 Finnis, J.M., 'A philosophical case against euthanasia' *op, cit.,*
    p.32.

19 Singer, P., *op. cit.,* pp.194-195.

20 *Ibid.*

21 *Ibid.*

22 Harris, J., *The Value of Life – An Introduction To Medical Ethics*
    (London: Routledge & Kegan Paul, 1985) p.17; Rachels, *op,
    cit.,* p.38.

23 Singer, P., *op, cit.,* p.194.

24 Foot, P., 'Euthanasia', *Philosophy & Public Affairs* **6** (1977) 100.

25 Rachels, J., *op, cit.,* p.26.

26 Foot, P., *op, cit.,* 105; Singer, *op cit.* p.196.

27 Maguire, D., 'Deciding for Yourself: The Objections' in Weir,
    R.F., (ed.), *Ethical Issues in Death and Dying* (New York:
    Columbia University Press, 1977) p.339.

28 Singer, P., *op, cit.,* p.195.

29 Oderberg, D.S., *op, cit.,* pp.55-58.

30 Singer, P., *op, cit.,* p.194.

31 *Ibid.,* p.195.

32 Dworkin, R., *Freedom's Law* (Oxford: Oxford University Press,
    1996) p.146.
    See also Harris, *op, cit.,* p.80; Engelhardt Jr., *op, cit.,* p.346;
    Beauchamp & Childress, *op, cit.,* p.236.

33 Steinbock, B., 'The Intentional Termination of Life' in Steinbock
    & Norcross (eds.) *op, cit.,* p.123.

34 Submission To The Select Committee Of The House Of Lords
    On Medical Ethics by The Linacre Centre For Healthcare Ethics
    (June 1993), www.linacre.org/lords.html p.10 of 34.

35 Finnis, J.M., 'A philosophical case against euthanasia', *op. cit.*, p.70.

36 Drinan, R.F., 'Should There Be a Legal Right to Die?' in Weir (ed.) *op, cit.*, p.302.

37 Engelhardt Jr. H.T., *op, cit.*, p.347.

38 Singer, P. *op, cit.*, pp.199-200. I am not certain whether Singer would prevent a rational individual taking heroin but in the passage I refer to he acknowledges limits to autonomy.

39 I would endorse Professor John Keown's distinction between quality of life which purports to judge the worthwhileness of the patient's life and quality of life which is the unavoidable assessment of a patient's condition prior to assessing the worthwhileness of a proposed treatment; Keown, 'Restoring Moral and Intellectual Shape to the Law...' *op. cit.*, 486-487.

40 Oderberg, D.S., *op, cit.*, p.60. See also, 'Submission To The Select Committee Of The House Of Lords On Medical Ethics' by The Linacre Centre, *op. cit.*, p.11 of 34.

41 Engelhardt, H.T., *op cit.*, p.349 – a quote attributed to Seneca.

42 Rachels, J., *op, cit.*, p.58.

43 *Ibid.*, p.67.

44 Dworkin, R., *op, cit.*, p.136.

45 *Ibid.*, p.142.

46 Keown, J., *op. cit.*, 481-503, particularly 486-487.

47 Rachels, J., *op, cit.*, p.113.

48 Engelhardt Jr., H.T., *op, cit.*, p.351.

49 Dyck, A.J., 'Alternative to Ethic of Euthanasia' in Weir (ed.) *op, cit.*, p.288.

50 Rachels, *op, cit.*, p.94.

51 *Ibid.*, p.105. See also Harris, J, 'The philosophical case against the philosophical case against euthanasia' in Keown (ed.), *op cit.*, pp.36-45.

52 Oderberg, D.S., *op, cit.*, p.76.

53 Sullivan, T.D., 'Coming to Terms: A Response to Rachels' in Steinbock & Norcross, *op cit.*, p.156; see also Finnis, J.M., 'Bland: Crossing the Rubicon' *L.Q.R.* **109** (1993) 331.

54 Steinbock, *op, cit.*, p.122.

55 Oderberg, D.S., *op, cit.*, p.77; Finnis, 'A philosophical case against euthanasia' *op, cit.*, p.27.

56 Foot, P., 'The Problem of Abortion and the Doctrine of the Double Effect' in Steinbock & Norcross, *op, cit.*, p.267.

57 See Beauchamp & Childress, *op, cit.*, p.207 for the four elements.

58 Finnis, J.M., 'A philosophical case against euthanasia' *op, cit.*, p.64.

59 Oderberg, D.S., *op, cit.*, p.81.

60 Kelly, G., S.J., *Theological Studies* 12, 'The Duty to Preserve Life', (1951) 550.

61 Oderberg, D.S., *op, cit.*, p.81.

62 Beauchamp & Childress, *op, cit.*, p.200.

63 Singer, P., *Rethinking Life and Death: The Collapse of Our Traditional Ethics* (Oxford: OUP, 1995), pp.71-72; Engelhardt Jr., *op, cit.*, p.342.

64 Steinbock, *op, cit.*, p.124.

65 Maguire, D., *op, cit.*, p.327.

66 Beauchamp & Childress, *op, cit.*, p.205.

67 Harris, J., 'Final Thoughts On Final Acts' in Keown (ed.), *op, cit.*, p.60.

68 Beauchamp & Childress, *op, cit.*, p.10.

69 Rachels, J., *op, cit.*, p.185.

70 Maguire, D., *op, cit.*, p.332.

71 Jochemsen, H., & Keown, J., *Journal of Medical Ethics* 25, 'Voluntary euthanasia under control? Further empirical evidence from the Netherlands', (1999) 16-21.

72 Gillon, R., *Journal of Medical Ethics* 25, 'Euthanasia in the Netherlands – down the slippery slope?' Editorial, (1999) 4.

73 Oderberg, D.S., *op, cit.*, p.68.

74 Dyck, A.J., *op, cit.*, p.291.

75 Harris, J., 'Euthanasia and The Value of Life' in Keown (ed.) *op, cit.*, p.20.

The Parliamentary battle

When the pro-life movement campaigns against abortion we often find ourselves fighting a lonely battle, not only against the militant feminist lobby but also against the medical establishment. So far, this has not been the case in our fight against euthanasia. In opposing the legalisation of euthanasia we have been joined by the British Medical Association, the Royal Colleges, Help the Aged, disability rights groups, the Archbishops of Canterbury and Westminster, and the Chief Rabbi.

All recognise that intentional killing, other than for the requirements of justice, is unethical. The prohibition against intentional killing is fundamental to our whole legal system. Legalising euthanasia in any way, shape or form would fatally undermine the prohibition. Allowing doctors to help their patients to die corrupts the doctor-patient relationship.

In the last few years the pro-euthanasia lobby,

in the form of the Voluntary Euthanasia Society (VES), has been focusing its parliamentary efforts on the House of Lords. Lord Joel Joffe, a former human rights lawyer from South Africa and a member of the VES for over thirty years, has introduced two Bills into the House of Lords in an attempt to legalise voluntary euthanasia – the Patient (Assisted Dying) Bill and the Assisted Dying for the Terminally Ill Bill.

The Patient (Assisted Dying) Bill sought to 'enable a competent adult who is suffering unbearably as a result of a terminal or a serious and progressive physical illness to receive medical help to die at his own considered and persistent request'. It made little progress so that in the next parliamentary session Lord Joffe introduced a revised version of this Bill.

The Assisted Dying for the Terminally Ill Bill, which the House of Lords is considering as I write, seeks to 'enable a competent adult who is suffering unbearably as a result of a terminal illness to receive medical assistance to die at his own considered and persistent request'.[1]

By, on the face of it, restricting the scope of the Assisted Dying for the Terminally Ill Bill, Lord Joffe and his pro-euthanasia allies have attempted to deal with the well-articulated fears of those opposed to the legalisation of euthanasia, not least the fears of disability rights groups. However, while the packaging may have changed, the contents remain the same. The effect of this Bill reaching the statute book would be devastating for the elderly, the terminally ill and those with disabilities. The parallels with the strategy and tactics pursued by the National Abortion Campaign throughout the 1950s and '60s could not be clearer – not least in the manipulation of tragic cases to soften parliamentary and public opinion.

Moves to legalise voluntary euthanasia are being driven by the tragic cases of individuals like Diane Pretty.

Diane was terminally ill with Motor Neurone Disease (MND), and she argued that her husband should be legally allowed to 'help her die' (i.e. kill her). She said that 'rather than die by choking or suffocation' she wanted to die at a time of her own choosing.[2] Throughout, Diane maintained that unless she was helped to die she would choke and suffocate to death. Fortunately this was, and is, not true. Dr Nigel Sykes, medical director of St Christopher's Hospice in London, the hospice founded by Dame Cicely Saunders, has said that not one of the 300 or so MND patients treated by him has ever suffocated.[3]

I recently attended a meeting of the All-Party

Parliamentary Group on Motor Neurone Disease. The meeting was addressed by Dr David Oliver, a Consultant in Palliative Medicine from Wisdom Hospice in Rochester, Kent. He informed us that in a survey conducted of 171 deaths from MND in the UK and Germany none choked to death. Dr Oliver finished his address with a quote from someone with MND who said, 'I have a difficult disease, I'm not a difficult patient.'

Diane Pretty's sad case received massive and prolonged publicity in the Press and media, almost all of it biased in favour of euthanasia, and this led most people to believe that it would be humane, in the words of the pro-euthanasia propaganda, to 'allow her to die with dignity'.

Diane took her case to the courts, arguing that if the Director of Public Prosecutions refused to grant immunity from punishment to her husband if he killed her, the Government would be subjecting her to 'inhuman and degrading treatment' in breach of the European Convention on Human Rights which the Government had incorporated into UK law through the Human Rights Act 1998.

Diane also argued that Article 2 of the European Convention on Human Rights which guarantees that 'everyone's right to life shall be protected by law. No one shall be deprived of his life intentionally...' also included a right to die with dignity.

Diane lost her case at each judicial stage, from the High Court through to the House of Lords and the European Court of Human Rights. In *Pretty v United Kingdom*,[4] the European Court of Human Rights had this to say about Diane's argument that Article 2, the right to life, also encompassed a 'right to die'! (emphasis added):

> The consistent emphasis in all the cases before the Court has been the obligation of the State to *protect* life. The Court is not persuaded that the 'right to life' guaranteed in Article 2 can be interpreted as involving a negative aspect. ...it is unconcerned with issues to do with the quality of living or what a person chooses to do with his or her life... nor can it create a right to self-determination in the sense of conferring on an individual the entitlement to choose death rather than life.

Shortly after losing her case at the European Court of Human Rights, her final court of appeal, Diane died on 11 May 2002 at a hospice near to her home in Luton. I am convinced that the timing of Diane's death was not coincidental. Having exhausted all judicial avenues Diane was finally able to 'let-go'. One wonders how much earlier she would have died if her court case had not been pursued to the extent it was.

Following Diane's death the VES and her husband Brian claimed that her death was not peaceful and painless, saying that she 'endured breathing difficulties, pain and distress'.[5]

However, Dr Ryszard Bietzk, Head of Medical Services at the Pasque Hospice, who actually cared for Diane Pretty during the last few days of her life, said 'Diane died peacefully... choking or suffocation was never an issue for her.'[6] According to Dr Bietzk, Diane's death was 'perfectly normal, natural and peaceful'.[7]

Diane's case was quickly followed in the media by that of Reginald Crew who, like her, was terminally ill with Motor Neurone disease. Using the services of the macabre Swiss organisation 'Dignitas' he travelled to Switzerland to take advantage of the ambiguity in the Swiss law on assisted suicide.

This law states: 'Whoever lures someone into suicide or provides assistance to commit suicide out of a self-interested motivation will, on completion of the suicide, be punished with up to five years' imprisonment.'[8] Dignitas interprets this to mean that anyone who assists suicide altruistically cannot be punished.

Not surprisingly, many in Switzerland strongly

oppose the group's activities and want to shrug off their country's reputation as Europe's foremost death tourism country. 'We do not want Switzerland to be a destination for tourism for suicide',[9] said Beatrice Wertli of the Swiss Christian Democrats.

One can see why when one considers the case of Jennifer and Bob Stokes from Hertfordshire. In Spring 2003 this married couple killed themselves by drinking a lethal dose of sodium pentobarbital in an assisted suicide in Zurich organised with the help of Dignitas.

According to a report in *The Sunday Times* the Stokes' deaths devastated their families, not least because neither Mr nor Mrs Stokes was terminally ill.[10] Nor were they wheelchair users and they certainly were not chronically depressed. 'Anger, hurt, bitterness, disbelief. You don't know which feelings will come out first.' These are the words of Jennifer Stokes' sister Dorothy. She goes on: 'Dignitas? It's got nothing to do with dignity – our sister ended up in a seedy little flat, lying on a twin bed.' If euthanasia were ever legalised in the United Kingdom these sentiments will become far more widespread.

Individuals like Diane Pretty, Reginald Crew and Jennifer and Bob Stokes were seduced by the manipulative arguments of the pro-euthanasia lobby into believing that their only choice was between euthanasia and an appallingly painful death. This ignores the fact that with proper palliative care, including properly managed pain relief, it is possible to die with dignity. We do not need doctors to kill us.

The story of Pamela Vack serves as a powerful retort to the claims of the pro-euthanasia lobby.

Like Diane Pretty, Pamela has MND. Pamela is a writer whom I met when she came into Parliament to talk to MPs and Peers about living with MND and why she is opposed to the legalisation of euthanasia.

Prior to the onset of MND Pamela was an active person. Her symptoms first presented themselves after she and her husband Hector had returned from a holiday in The Gambia. Feeling very anxious and unwell, Pamela visited a neurologist who told her that she had contracted a virus in her central nervous system. As the years passed Pamela's symptoms and muscle weakness became progressively worse. She saw many consultants who considered the possibility of her developing Multiple Sclerosis and then Muscular Dystrophy before Pamela was finally diagnosed with Atypical MND.

Once the diagnosis of MND was confirmed, Pamela knew that she would encounter increasingly difficulties with speech, swallowing and chewing and that her muscles would become weak and floppy. She describes her current situation as follows:

> My upper trunk requires a good deal of support and propping up, and my wheelchair is more frequently in use as my legs let me know that exercise and walking are not helpful, but no longer on the agenda! Gradually one loses movement altogether and considerable help is required in lifting even a cup, in bathing and dressing. Altogether, every Motor Neurone sufferer faces the frequent frustration of not being able to keep one's independence in coping with simple tasks.

Pamela is under no illusions about how difficult it can be to live with a debilitating illness such as MND. Following the Diane Pretty case through the media, Pamela told me that she felt 'compelled to speak out against the insidious campaign to have our laws changed allowing assisted suicide'. As a result Pamela has appeared on national radio and television as a powerful advocate against euthanasia which, she believes, would place 'a huge number of elderly, disabled and vulnerable people at risk'. Perhaps more importantly, she has sought to reassure society and particularly MND patients that they need not succumb to the despair and hopelessness that seemed to characterise the Diane Pretty campaign.

On a number of occasions when Pamela has been interviewed by the media she has been, as she says, 'taunted' with words to the effect that once she reaches the end stages of MND she will change her mind and support euthanasia and assisted suicide. Nothing could be further from the truth. 'I am completely confident that when and if I require pain relief and medication, they will be offered – even ventilation. "Choking to death" is very rarely an issue with MND, and is often used to promote fear through the lobby for euthanasia.' Pamela also counts herself fortunate that in the UK we have perhaps the finest hospice movement in the world offering 'expertise, kindness and understanding during those final stages, helping patients to die with dignity… We need to inform and reassure those with terminal illness that this is a fact.'

Supported by her husband Hector, and sustained by her Christian faith, Pamela told me that:

> Life is God given – our times are in His hands. It is not to be 'snuffed out' when the going becomes difficult, when some elderly

infirm may well feel a burden to family and friends. Let us value those who suffer a disability, mental or physical, and offer the help that is needed to improve their lives, making those later years worthwhile, and learning the lessons of endurance, perseverance and wisdom that only they can teach us.

It was stories such as Pamela's that, in 1994, persuaded the distinguished House of Lords Select Committee on Medical Ethics to unanimously recommend that:

> There should be no change in law to permit euthanasia.[11]

> We recommend no change in law on assisted suicide.[12]

The conclusions of the Select Committee on Medical Ethics are as pertinent now as they were a decade ago. We ignore them at our peril. The members of this Select Committee recognised that society's prohibition of intentional killing is 'the cornerstone of law and of social relation-ships'.[13] The Select Committee correctly noted that the prohibition on intentional killing 'protects each one of us impartially, embodying the belief that all are equal'.[14] They had no wish to see that protection diminished.

Were voluntary euthanasia to be legalised this 'cornerstone of law and of social relationships' would vanish overnight with disastrous consequences for the most vulnerable in our society. As the British Medical Association has observed, it would fatally corrupt the doctor-patient relationship – a relationship founded upon trust.

> The BMA has consistently opposed euthanasia and physician-assisted suicide... we believe that in the case of euthanasia and assisted suicide, benefit for an individual in terms of having their wishes respected, is only achievable at too high a cost in terms of potential harm to society at large.[15]

Doctors would become killers as well as carers. Vulnerable patients would be left not knowing whether the doctor coming to visit them at their bedside was acting in his role as carer or killer.

It would be impossible not to be moved by the tragic cases of Diane Pretty and Reginald Crew. I recognise the suffering of patients with Motor Neurone Disease and similarly debilitating diseases and acknowledge the anguish of the families who care for loved ones with these conditions. Any of us who have lived with people we love who have been affected by acute suffering cannot fail to be touched by the personal consequences that arise.

However, the conclusions of the Select Committee on Medical Ethics about whether individual personal cases should determine public policies must not be forgotten:

> Individual cases cannot reasonably establish the foundation of a policy (the legalisation of euthanasia) which would have such serious and widespread repercussions... the issue of euthanasia is one in which the interest of the individual cannot be separated from the interest of society as a whole.[16]

As disability rights groups, including the Disability Rights Commission and Disability Awareness in Action, have pointed out, if we authorise voluntary euthanasia and assisted suicide for Multiple Sclerosis or Motor Neurone Disease sufferers, how will this impact upon those individuals who have these conditions and do not wish to die? Will they feel under pressure to seek an assisted, premature death?

The latest empirical evidence from the Netherlands contained in the official report by Van der Wal and Van der Maas[17] notes that the frequency of ending of life without the patient's explicit request has shown no decline over the years studied: 1990, 1995 and 2001. In 2001, the most recent year for statistics available, 900 out of 3,800 cases of euthanasia or assisted suicide (approximately one-quarter) were without the patient's explicit request. Where was the patient autonomy that the VES is so keen to promote in these cases?

These official statistics also show that only 54 per cent of all cases of euthanasia are reported to the proper authorities. More worryingly still, at a meeting in the House of Lords in Spring 2003 organised by the VES Professor Griffiths of the Faculty of Law, University of Gröningen admitted that it is the 'more problematic' cases that are escaping the control system. So much for legalisation introducing greater control!

One case from the Netherlands is particularly disturbing. A Dutch GP, Van Ooijen, was placed on trial because he had terminated the life of a nursing home patient at the request of the family rather than the patient. Van Ooijen was found guilty of murder, yet not punished because he acted 'with integrity'!

The wealth of disturbing evidence emanating from the Netherlands led the prestigious *Journal of Medical Ethics*, a periodical not known for its pro-life sympathies, to declare in an editorial:

Restrictions on euthanasia that legal controls in the Netherlands were supposed to have implemented are being extensively ignored and from that point of view it is surely justifiable to conclude... that the practice of euthanasia in the Netherlands is in poor control; and in particular, that as well as voluntary euthanasia... involuntary and non-voluntary euthanasia are also being carried out.[18]

The equally prestigious *British Medical Journal* has reported that delegates at the World Medical Association conference compared Dutch policy to 'practices from the Third Reich'. The World Medical Association subsequently passed a resolution declaring voluntary euthanasia to be contrary to 'basic ethical principles of medical practice', strongly encouraging all doctors and medical associations not to participate in euthanasia 'even if national law allows it'.[19]

The Dutch experience contradicts the claim that legalisation 'brings euthanasia out of the closet' and subjects it to regulation. It simply produces more euthanasia, not more control.

This is why, to go back to the point I made at the beginning of this chapter, moves to legalise voluntary euthanasia are overwhelmingly opposed by a broad coalition of those individuals and organisations that would be affected most: the elderly, the terminally ill, disabled people and the medical profession.

In a letter sent to members of the House of Lords, Help the Aged expressed strong opposition to Lord Joffe's Patient (Assisted Dying) Bill, categorically stating that 'we do not support changes to the law relating to euthanasia'. Age Concern are similarly opposed to any change in the law.

Amongst those who care for the terminally ill in our hospice movement, opposition to euthanasia is resolute. Speaking at the time the House of Lords was debating Lord Joffe's Patient (Assisted Dying) Bill, Dr Nigel Sykes, medical director of St Christopher's Hospice in London, declared that: 'Euthanasia is a minority interest amongst the terminally ill. It is only those who are healthy who want Lord Joffe's Bill.'[20] Professor David Currow, Professor of Palliative and Supportive Services at Australia's Flinders University, insists that despair and depression – not pain – are the main reason why people end their lives: 'If you're not depressed or demoralised your chance of seeking euthanasia is zero.'[21]

Those who care for the terminally ill in our hospice movement maintain that with proper care, patients *should not* die in pain. In the

Netherlands, surveys have shown that pain is very low down on the reasons for requesting euthanasia. Positive requests for euthanasia usually result from poor medical care. When good palliative care is offered there is a dramatic drop in requests. A recent independent survey of doctors revealed that two-thirds of doctors considered that the pressure for euthanasia would be lessened if there were more resources for the hospice movement.[22]

In 2003 the Association of Palliative Medicine and the National Council for Hospice and Specialist Palliative Care Services published a briefing paper on euthanasia and physician-assisted suicide.[23] In it they argued that euthanasia, once accepted,

> ...is uncontrollable for philosophical, logical and practical reasons rather than slippery slopes of moral laxity or idleness. Patients will certainly die without and against their wishes if any such legislation is introduced. This will proceed out of what will be a doctor's revised duty to kill, in situations of unbearable suffering or where they are seen to be in the patient's best interests, according to the redefinition of active killing as a potential clinical and societal good.

I would also cite a recent article in the *British Medical Journal* in which the authors conclude that 'the desire for euthanasia must not be taken at face value':[24]

> Rather than focusing on assessing the mental competence of patients requesting euthanasia or determining clear legal guidelines, doctors must acquire the skills for providing good end of life care. These include the ability to 'connect' with patients, diagnose suffering, and understand patients' hidden agendas through in-depth exploration. This is especially important as the tenor of care influences patients' perception of hope and self worth. There is much to ponder over the meaning of a euthanasia request before we have to consider its justification.

Unbearable pain and suffering seem to be the hoop through which one has to jump for euthanasia to be acceptable to some. Yet, as Dr Andrew Lawson, a Consultant in Anaesthesia and Pain Management has observed:

> How much pain and of what kind do I have to have for it to be enough of a burden to be allowed to die? Surely it would be discriminatory to suggest that only in certain

circumstances can euthanasia be allowed. One would in effect have to prove to someone else's satisfaction that one's quality of life was so bad. This would inevitably involve a subjective judgement which would diminish individual choice.[25]

The Hospice Movement is adamant that the law does not need to be changed for patients to receive comprehensive and effective management of distress and agitation. 'To infer otherwise is misleading and mischievous.'[26]

Euthanasia cannot be limited except by arbitrary and discriminatory regulations. It would quickly become a symptom control choice, one option of treatment among others.

And what about the opinions of the medical profession? Doctors and nurses, after all, would be responsible for killing patients were euthanasia and assisted suicide ever legalised. The most recent independent survey of medical opinion carried out by Opinion Research Business (ORB) and published on 13 May 2003[27] shows that there is little demand from the medical profession for legislation of this nature. Almost three out of four doctors (74 per cent) would refuse to perform assisted suicide if it were legalised. A clear majority of doctors also consider that it would be impossible to set safe bounds to euthanasia.

The survey explodes the idea that many people are clamouring for euthanasia. In response to a question asking how many patients had requested euthanasia during the past three years nearly half (48 per cent) of the doctors said not one. 37 per cent quoted less than five; 11 per cent gave numbers between five and ten patients; only 2 per cent gave figures of more than ten.

We must not allow individual cases such as those of Diane Pretty and Reginald Crew to establish the foundation of a misguided policy which is feared and opposed by those whom it will affect the most. Time and again hard cases have been used to make thoroughly bad law.

Parliament is in grave danger of being seduced by a plethora of dubious opinion polls from the VES claiming that the legalisation of voluntary euthanasia has broad public support. Yet amongst those whom legalised euthanasia would affect the most – the elderly, the terminally ill and the disabled – there is overwhelming opposition.

Intentional killing is unethical. Those who support voluntary euthanasia have to provide any compelling reasons why society's prohibition on intentional killing should be set aside. To date, such reasons have not been forthcoming. It is impossible to establish an effective regulatory framework for assisted suicide and euthanasia. By allowing a few patients to receive medical help to die we would be putting large numbers of patients at grave risk.

NOTES

1 For the full text of the Bill see:
http://www.publications.parliament.uk/pa/ld200304/ldbills/017/04017.1-4.html#j01

2 *Ananova*, "Husband urges Blair to back euthanasia" (22 June 2001); http://www.ananova.com/

3 Address given by Dr Nigel Sykes at Ecumenical Meeting in St George's R.C. Church, Walthamstow, East London (13 November 2003).

4 Application No. 2346/02; paragraph 39 of the Judgement.

5 Letter from Brian Pretty in *The Congleton Chronicle* (1 July 2002).

6 Edwards, L., 'The last days of Diane Pretty', *The Luton Herald & Post* (15 May 2002).

7 http://news.bbc.co.uk/1/hi/health/1983941.stm

8 http://news.bbc.co.uk/1/hi/world/europe/2676837.stm

9 *Ibid.*

10 McFerran, A., 'How could our sister plan her own death?' in *The Sunday Times* (20 April 2003), News Review Section, p.7.

11 Report of the Select Committee on Medical Ethics; HL Paper 21-I, Session 1993-94. London: HMSO. Para. 278.

12 *Ibid.* Para. 295.

13 *Ibid.* Para. 237.

14 *Ibid.*

15 BMA Briefing on the Assisted Dying for the Terminally Ill Bill: http://www.bma.org.uk/ap.nsf/Content/Assisteddying

16 Report of the Select Committee on Medical Ethics; *op. cit.* Para. 237.

17 G. Van der Wal and P. Van der Maas, Chapter 19 of their report on euthanasia, 2003. See also Dr Bregje D. Onwuteaka-Phillipsen et al, 'Euthanasia and other end of life decisions in the Netherlands in 1990, 1995 and 2001', *The Lancet* (17 June 2003); http://image.thelancet.com/extras/03art3297web.pdf

18 Gillon, R., 'Euthanasia in the Netherlands – down the slippery slope?' Editorial, *Journal of Medical Ethics* 25 (1999) 4.

19 Sheldon, T., *British Medical Journal* 2002, 'World Medical Association isolates Netherlands on euthanasia', 325:675 (28 September 2002).

20 Address given by Dr Nigel Sykes in the Moses Room, House of Lords (7 May 2003).

21 Address given by Professor Currow to a meeting in the House of Lords (1 April 2003).

22 Survey on Euthanasia and Assisted Suicide Prepared for 'Right to Life' lobby group. Results from 986 interviews 26 March – 9 April 2003. Opinion Research Business, 9-13 Cursitor Street, London, EC4A 1LL; www.opinion.co.uk

23 The Patient (Assisted Dying) Bill: A joint briefing paper by the Association for Palliative Medicine and the National Council for Hospice and Specialist Palliative Care Services (May 2003). Presented in the House of Lords on 3 June 2003.

24 Mak, Y.Y.W. Elwyn, G. and Finlay, I.G., *British Medical Journal* (26 July 2003), 'Patients' voices are needed in debates on euthanasia', 327:213-215.

25 Letter to the Editor, *The Daily Telegraph* (18 April 2003, p.27).

26 The Patient (Assisted Dying) Bill: A joint briefing paper by the Association for Palliative Medicine and the National Council for Hospice and Specialist Palliative Care Services (May 2003). Presented in the House of Lords on 3 June 2003.

27 Survey on Euthanasia and Assisted Suicide Prepared for 'Right to Life' lobby group. Results from 986 interviews 26 March – 9 April 2003. Opinion Research Business, 9-13 Cursitor Street, London, EC4A 1LL; www.opinion.co.uk

Tony Bland and Anthony Devine – Despair and hope

In previous chapters I have considered the philosophical and practical arguments against voluntary euthanasia and assisted suicide. In such cases you have a competent adult like Diane Pretty or Reginald Crew who is asking for help to die usually by way of lethal injection or overdose. Thankfully the law in the UK has not acceded to the requests of such adults. To date the law has not accepted this argument and Parliament has declined to change it.

However, this is not to say that euthanasia is entirely illegal in this country. Non-voluntary euthanasia refers to the killing of an individual, supposedly in his or her 'best interests', when that individual is not in a position to express a view one way or another on the matter, that is to say, they are mentally incapacitated.

Until 1993, the common law in this country was quite clear. It was always wrong to have as the purpose of one's conduct the bringing about of another person's death, after birth, for any reason other than the requirements of justice. That common law principle is enshrined in Article 2 of the European Convention on Human Rights. Prior to 1993 it was a clearly understood part of the common law that murder can be committed not only by a positive act, but also by omission in situations where there is a duty to provide what is omitted. This covered doctors who owe their patients a duty of care.

So what happened in 1993 to change all of this? To answer this question we need to go back to 15 April 1989.

Anthony Bland was a seventeen-year-old fan of Liverpool Football Club. Along with friends he attended the now infamous F.A. Cup Semi-Final between Liverpool and Nottingham Forest at the Hillsborough football ground in Sheffield when 96 people died. Tony, as he was known, became caught in the crush at the Leppings Lane end of the Hillsborough ground. He suffered severe injuries. The part of his brain necessary for thinking and feeling was extensively and permanently damaged due to lack of oxygen. However, he was neither dead, nor dying. His brain stem was still functioning; he was breathing unassisted and digested food that was supplied through a tube.

His doctors and parents wanted to stop the feeding and medical care on the grounds that it served no useful purpose. The courts were asked to adjudicate and on 4 February 1993, the House of Lords upheld a previous declaration that it would be lawful to withdraw feeding and medical care.[1] Tube feeding was withdrawn from Tony Bland and he died of renal failure, consequent on dehydration, on 3 March 1993.

Their Lordships held that to stop feeding Tony Bland was an omission. Tube feeding was medical treatment which the doctors were under no duty to provide because it was not in the patient's best interests, was futile, and was a course of conduct endorsed by a responsible body of medical opinion.

The purpose of stopping tube feeding was to put an end to the life of Tony Bland. This is why the decision of the House of Lords in his case amounts to the legalisation of a form of non-voluntary euthanasia. Prior to Bland, such conduct was incompatible with the duty of care owed to a patient. Following Bland, conduct aimed at ending a patient's life, providing it counts as an omission, may well be deemed as compatible with the exercise of the duty of care for a patient if doctors judge that patient's life no longer worthwhile.

In the Bland case three out of the five Law Lords acknowledged – the others not dissenting – that the aim or purpose of withdrawing tube feeding was to bring about Tony Bland's death.

In a long quotation one of the Law Lords, Lord Mustill, said:

It is essential to face up squarely to the true nature of what is proposed… Emollient expressions such as 'letting nature take its course' and 'easing the passing' may have their uses, but they are out of place here, for they conceal both the ethical and the legal issues, and I will try to avoid them… The conclusion that the declarations can be upheld depends crucially on a distinction drawn by the criminal law between acts and omissions, and carries with it inescapably a distinction between, on the one hand what is often called 'mercy killing', where active steps are taken in a medical context to terminate the life of a suffering patient, and a situation such as the present where the proposed conduct has the aim for equally humane reasons of terminating the life of Anthony Bland by withholding from him the basic necessities of life. The acute unease which I feel about adopting this way through the legal and ethical maze is I believe due in an important part to the sensation that however much the terminologies may differ the ethical status of the two courses of action is for all relevant purposes indistinguishable.[2]

Patients in the permanently unconscious condition Tony Bland was in are not the only individuals to have been adversely affected by that judgement. Gradually it has been extended to cover other patients. In June 1999 the British Medical Association (BMA) published guidance on *Withholding and Withdrawing Life-prolonging Medical Treatment* in which they considered it appropriate to withdraw tube feeding from 'patients who have suffered a stroke or have severe dementia'. This guidance has received support from the General Medical Council (GMC) in its 2002 publication, *Withholding and Withdrawing Life-prolonging Treatments: Good Practice in Decision-making*.[3]

Tube feeding or sustenance is not medical treatment. It is basic care. Many people with cystic fibrosis are fed by gastric tube and live an otherwise normal life. Others with paralysis of the throat and swallowing mechanism feed via nasal tubes. Great progress has been made by nurses, doctors, dieticians and speech therapists working together to help those with swallowing difficulties. If swallowing is impossible, thirst should be relieved by fluids delivered by the least invasive method possible in the circumstances.

Tube feeding is being withdrawn from patients like Tony Bland or those who have suffered a stroke or have severe dementia because doctors and others judge that their lives are no longer worthwhile. This is wholly incompatible with the respect for the worth and dignity of every human being which forms the basis of our laws.

To allow doctors to withdraw sustenance from patients with the purpose of ending their lives subverts the law of murder.

Tony Bland's case can be starkly contrasted with the case of one of my former constituents in Liverpool, Andrew Devine. Andrew was one of my constituents who were injured or died at Hillsborough. Like Tony Bland, Andrew went into a deep coma. Their conditions were identical. Shortly after the Hillsborough tragedy I visited Andrew and his parents. As the years passed I have followed Andrew's progress. In 2003, prior to a parliamentary debate on this subject, I asked Andrew's mother whether I could tell Parliament what had happened to him in the intervening fourteen years during which she and her husband had fought for Andrew's life, and she gave me her permission. Mrs Devine told me that having been told by medics that, 'Andrew will never be able to swallow or to eat food', she felt that her son had 'been written off'. She was told that it 'would be a waste of resources to treat him'.

The medics also said that it would be clear within two years whether Andrew was going to make any progress. In fact, it took five years. They told his parents 'nothing can be done' when quite a lot could be done and was done.

Some of you may recall the front page story from *The Guardian* in 1997 when Andrew's parents talked publicly about the improvements that had taken place in his health. Against all the predictions Andrew now eats heartily and eats solids. Mrs Devine is adamant that 'from our point of view it was a hard enough battle to fight for the things we needed without being offered the chance to do away with Andrew'. She says, 'Starving or dehydrating someone is an unpleasant death – you might as well give a lethal injection.'

Through their love and devotion Andrew's parents discovered the Brain Injury Rehabilitation and Development Centre at Broughton, near Chester, not because they were referred there, but because they found it via a television pro-gramme. They took Andrew to London, to the Royal Hospital for Neuro-disability at West Hill in Putney and paid for his first course of treatment themselves.

Mrs Devine argues that the law needs to be strengthened in the light of the Tony Bland decision to stop the practice of non-voluntary euthanasia through the withdrawal of food and fluids delivered by artificial means, conveniently re-defined as 'medical treatment'. Otherwise, 'economic pressures to free beds would be overwhelming; the pressure would be enormous'.

Since 1993 I have strongly supported efforts within Parliament to reverse the Bland decision or, at the very least, mitigate its disastrous consequences. Regularly, when I have sought to highlight the injustice of withdrawing or withholding food and fluids from non-dying patients on the spurious grounds that this would be in the patient's best interests, I have been invited to tilt at what I consider to be imaginary windmills.

I have never argued that we must go to 'heroic lengths' or apply extraordinary means to keep patients alive. After all, as Christians we believe that death is the beginning of a new life with God and therefore not something to be fought for at all costs. We are under no obligation to keep alive someone who would otherwise die. But undoubtedly, if we reclassify food and fluid as a burdensome treatment, then we shall sanction euthanasia.

In March 2003 a letter appeared in *The Times* which gets to the nub of the issue. The correspondent wrote that:

> Many of us assumed that nutritional requirements of patients in hospital were so fundamental we would not even imagine that there was a lack of such service... If something so basic is not given priority it is little wonder that many other aspects of hospital care are ignored, such as cleanliness and hygiene. How can management allow such ineptitude to exist?[4]

Food and fluids have, until recently, always been regarded as basic care to which everyone is entitled. We should be under no illusions that acceptance of the withdrawal of food and fluids from non-dying patients has consistently been identified by the pro-euthanasia lobby as the precursor to the legalisation of positive euthanasia. Speaking at the Fifth Biennial Congress of Societies for the Right to Die in September 1984, Dr Helgha Kuhse, a pro-euthanasia bioethicist, declared; 'If we can get people to accept the removal of all treatment and care – especially the removal of food and fluids – they will see what a painful way this is to die and then, in the patient's best interests, they will accept the lethal injection.'

Dr Kuhse's views are shared by Professor Sheila McLean, an academic lawyer from Glasgow University, a significant contributor to the BMA Guidelines on *Withholding and Withdrawing Life-prolonging Medical Treatment* and a member of the VES who has referred to Bland and subsequent court judgements as a form of non-voluntary euthanasia.[5]

The killing of non-dying patients in a persistent vegetative state – PVS – and similar conditions by the withdrawal or withholding of food and fluids has meant that there is an urgent need to restore integrity and coherence to the law of homicide. Otherwise Dr Kuhse's chilling statement will become a reality.

It is simply not good enough to say that killing patients is already illegal therefore there is no need to strengthen the law. The decision of the House of Lords in Bland, its confirmation in subsequent cases and the guidance emanating from the BMA and GMC have left the law, in the words of Lord Mustill, 'both morally and intellectually misshapen'.[6] To allow doctors to withdraw sustenance from patients with the purpose of ending their lives subverts the law of murder. Hence the urgent need for reform of the law.

In all the time that I have been debating this

matter, both inside and outside of Parliament, I have yet to hear a convincing explanation as to why food and fluids, however so delivered, should be classified as medical treatment and not basic care. What medical ailment is being treated? Since when has hunger or thirst been considered an illness? It has even been established in the case of animals that freedom from hunger and freedom from thirst constitute two of the five welfare considerations to which all domestic animals are entitled. Surely it is not unreasonable for the same criteria to be applied to human beings.

It is deeply paradoxical that in March 2003, just prior to a parliamentary debate on this issue, a shepherd was sentenced to six months in prison for not providing enough food and water for his sheep. If that had been a human being he would at least have been worth a judgement in the House of Lords!

Patients' groups such 'SOS-NHS', believe that elderly patients with dementia or strokes are most at risk from the premature withdrawal or withholding of food and fluids. 'SOS-NHS' are especially concerned about the increasingly common practice of sedating patients and then deliberately withholding nutrition and hydration until the patient dies. Having been sedated, the patient is unable to demand sustenance and his or her distress may not be readily apparent. The death certificate will commonly state that the cause of death was the underlying medical condition, not dehydration.

In February 2003, Radio 4's 'File on Four' programme drew attention to that worrying practice. Citing disturbing examples of over-sedation and the withdrawal of food and water, the programme makers suggested that they raised wider questions about the effectiveness of checks and controls in our care homes and about how we care for our ever-increasing number of elderly citizens. Such practices must end.

If non-dying patients are denied food and fluids then the inevitable consequence is death within days, whatever the pathology. By calling food and fluids delivered by artificial means medical treatment the courts, the Government, the BMA and the GMC have over-medicalised sustenance and have opened the way to the killing of vulnerable, particularly elderly, patients in our hospitals. Regardless of whether nutrition and hydration is delivered by a spoon, by PEG, or by nasogastric tube, it does not alter the substance of what is being delivered. The means of delivery may be artificial – not the sustenance itself. To talk of artificial nutrition and hydration is a complete misnomer.

Even the judges in Bland recognised this. Lord Hoffmann, in his judgement, declared as follows:

> If someone allows a small child or invalid in his care to starve to death, we do not say that he allowed nature to take its course. We think that he has committed a particularly wicked crime. We treat him as if he had introduced an external agency of death. It is the same ethical principle which requires doctors and hospitals to provide patients in their care with such medical attention and nursing as they are reasonably able to give… The giving of food to a helpful person is so much the quintessential example of kindness and humanity that it is hard to imagine a case in which it would be morally right to withhold it.[7]

What is needed therefore is some clear statement in the law that no person responsible for the care of another person is entitled to withdraw or withhold sustenance (however so delivered) from that person if his purpose in so doing is to hasten or otherwise cause the person's death. This would not create any new offence but would give a clear signal that notwithstanding the judgement in Bland, our legal prohibition against euthanasia is not to be weakened any further.

Such a clarificatory statement would not obstruct good medical practice. It would not impose any requirement on doctors to strive to keep alive patients who are dying. The role of doctors in terminal illness is to provide as peaceful and pain-free a death as possible. Doctors would still be able to withhold or withdraw sustenance from a patient who is in the process of dying, where the risk or discomfort of the placement of feeding tubes would be regarded as unduly intrusive or excessive. Such a practice is far removed from the deliberate withholding or withdrawing of sustenance with the purpose of causing the death of a patient who is not otherwise dying.

The last thing that I want is good doctors being exposed to complaints or the risk of prosecution at the behest of aggrieved relatives. That is why purpose is the key. When sustenance is withdrawn for ethically and legally acceptable reasons, the data about a patient's clinical condition and the observations of other carers will support the person responsible for the care of the patient.

Nor would clarifying the law as I suggest restrict patient autonomy. A doctor's respect for a competent patient's refusal of sustenance would involve no intention on his part other than a concern not to commit an assault, of which he would be guilty in imposing sustenance contrary to a competent patient's wishes.

Building on this concept of patient autonomy, there are those who believe that the best way to protect vulnerable mentally incapacitated adults like Tony Bland is to allow them, when competent, to sign an advance directive or 'living will', setting out what treatment they would refuse in the event of lacking mental capacity. Alternatively, it is suggested that they could appoint a health care proxy by way of a lasting power of attorney. In the event of the donor of the lasting power of attorney becoming mentally incapable, the proxy would have authority to step into the donor's shoes and direct the health care team as to what treatment should or should not be provided.

'Living wills' and lasting powers of attorney may appear superficially attractive but rather than enhance patient autonomy I have serious fears that they could actually undermine it.

It is generally accepted in principle that a patient can give an advance refusal of treatment and there can be no objection to doctors following a refusal which is recent, well-informed and is not suicidally motivated. However, the same cannot be said of a refusal which is made on the basis of inadequate information and/or has the aim of ending life.

It is a key principle of informed consent and good medical practice that a patient must have an explanation of the risks and benefits of a specified treatment, as well as an explanation of the potential consequences of refusal of that treatment (if a patient indicates they wish to refuse treatment).[8] Sadly, in the majority of advance refusals of treatment which are currently being proposed by various organisations, there is no way to establish what understanding the patient had of the risks and benefits of treatment, and more significantly whether they were fully aware of the consequences of refusal. Advance directives rarely, if ever, meet the standards of informed consent that are required from patients with capacity. An ill-informed advance decision can hardly be considered a genuine exercise of autonomy.

'Living wills' or legally binding advance refusals of treatment will make it very difficult for practitioners faced with the need to make rapid decisions in acute medical emergencies to easily and clearly decide when an advance directive is valid and applicable. Fear of litigation may well result in doctors withholding appropriate care with resultant harm to the patient. If doctors are legally obliged to respect ill-advised, vague, but apparently binding advance refusals it is the patient concerned who will suffer.

Baroness Finlay of Llandaff, a Professor of Palliative Medicine and a passionate opponent of euthanasia shares my concern:

> Advance refusals are very helpful for communicating with patients. It is terribly helpful as an idea of what patients want. My concern is that they are legally binding and then you may have to sit back and watch something happen that you just feel terribly uncomfortable with.[9]

A paper published in the *British Medical Journal* in November 2003 highlighted the problems with advance directives.[10] When presented with an advance directive that applied to the same hypothetical scenario, health professionals came to divergent conclusions as to the 'right thing to do'. Although four participants cited the potential value of advance directives in offering legal protection to the doctor who went against a family by withholding treatment, only one participant was in favour of statutory legislation.

One prospective study showed that in most cases advance directives were not consulted by carers in critical care situations.[11]

It is for these reasons that I oppose making advance refusals of treatment or 'living wills' legally binding. Non-legally binding advance refusals can, however, be very helpful to patients, their families and the healthcare team.

I am also extremely sceptical that health care proxies appointed by way of lasting powers of attorney will enhance patient autonomy or do anything to protect people like Tony Bland. Is it right, after all, that a non-medically qualified proxy should be automatically entitled to override the medical decision of the healthcare team, particularly when this proxy may have power over the patient's financial affairs and may benefit financially from his death?

Professor Sheila McLean, no friend of the pro-life lobby, had this to say about proxy decision making: 'All the evidence is that proxy decision makers get it wrong more often than they get it right, but that they do so in good faith.' She went on:

> We know that proxy decision makers are pretty inaccurate. Most of the research on this subject has been done in the United States. If the person who has appointed the proxy is asked what they would want the proxy to say, and then the proxy is asked what they think that

the person would want them to do, the evidence is that there is very little congruence between the two views.[12]

A far more effective way of protecting the interests of vulnerable adults would be to create a system of statutory consultees. The patient, or, in the event of the patient being unable to appoint anyone, an independent third party, could appoint another person to act on their behalf in the event of them becoming mentally incapacitated. The healthcare team would be bound to consult with this consultee on pain of professional and criminal/civil sanctions for wilfully failing to do so. Decisions reached by the consultee would not be legally binding upon medical staff. Nevertheless in the event of a dispute, the healthcare team would need to produce good reasons why the decision of the statutory consultee should not be respected.

Anthony Devine's parents would, for example, have benefited greatly from having their role as carers formally recognised. Ultimately, however, if non-dying patients are to be protected from the withdrawal or withholding of food and fluids, then what is needed is some clear statement in the law that no person responsible for the care of another person is entitled to withdraw or withhold sustenance (however so delivered) from that person if his purpose in so doing is to hasten or otherwise cause the person's death.

The 1994 House of Lords Select Committee on Medical Ethics concluded that the Bland judgement should not be enshrined in statute. It stated:

> We consider that the progressive development and ultimate acceptance of the notion that some treatment is inappropriate should make it unnecessary to consider the withdrawal of nutrition and hydration, except in circumstances where its administration is in itself evidently burdensome to the patient.[13]

Sadly, its conclusions have been ignored by the Government, and the withdrawal of nutrition and hydration from non-dying patients has become an accepted element of medical practice. Food and water are basic human needs that should never be withdrawn or withheld if the purpose in so doing is to hasten or otherwise cause the death of the patient.

The pro-euthanasia lobby sees acceptance of the withdrawal or withholding of sustenance from patients who are not dying as the first major hurdle to overcome on the road towards the legalisation of assisted suicide and positive euthanasia. After all, they argue, if it is legitimate to subject patients to a slow, painful and distressing death by starvation and dehydration, surely it is more compassionate to give them a lethal injection that will ensure a swift death?

Recognising the intrinsic dignity of each and every person, we must strive to change the prevailing culture in medicine and society. Faced with patients in PVS, or with dementia, or with stroke, our question should be: 'is this treatment worthwhile?' If, instead, we continue to pose the question: 'is this life worthwhile?' then the consequences for the disabled, elderly and terminally ill in society will be disastrous.

NOTES

1 Airedale NHS Trust v Bland [1993] A.C. 789.

2 Airedale NHS Trust v Bland [1993] A.C. 789 at 887.

3 On 30 July 2004 the High Court declared sections of the General Medical Council guidance to be contrary to Article 3 of the European Convention on Human Rights. Burke v The General Medical Council [2004] EWHC 1879 (Admin).

4 Letters to the Editor, *The Times* (12 March 2003, p.23).

5 http://www.catholicdoctors.org.uk/By_Topic/Euthanasia/winterton_bill_lettomps.htm

6 Airedale NHS Trust v Bland [1993] A.C. 789 at 887.

7 Airedale NHS Trust v Bland [1993] A.C. 789 at 831.

8   I suggest that the judgement of Mr Justice Hughes in the case Re: AK High Court of Justice, Family Division: Hughes J. (2000) 58 B.M.L.R. 151; [2001] 1 FLR 129 provides a useful framework for the recognition of advance refusals of treatment.

9   Oral evidence to the Joint Committee on the Draft Mental Incapacity Bill Session 2002-03 HL Paper 189-II; http://www.publications.parliament.uk/pa/jt200203/jtselect/jtdmi/189/3100901.htm

10 Thompson, T., Barbour, R., Schwartz, L., 'Adherence to advance directives in critical care decision making: vignette study', *British Medical Journal* 2003, 327:1011.

11 Danis et al, 'A prospective study of advance directives for life-sustaining care', *New England Journal of Medicine* 1991, 324:882-8.

12 Scottish Justice and Home Affairs Committee Official Report of Evidence Session on 17 November 1999. Evidence given to the Committee by Professor McLean; http://www.scottish.parliament.uk/S1/official_report/cttee/just 99-00/ju99-1002.htm

13 Report of the Select Committee on Medical Ethics; HL Paper 21-I, Session 1993-94. London: HMSO, para. 257.

'Our lives are worth living!'

In the spring of 2003, prior to a debate on Lord Joffe's Patient Assisted Dying Bill, I received a letter from Dr Jane Campbell, a disability rights commissioner and chairwoman of the Social Care Institute for Excellence.

> Disabled peoples' lives are invariably seen as less worthwhile than those of non-disabled people. Descriptions such as tragic, burdensome and even desperate are routinely used without objection... If suicide were a legally and socially acceptable option, too many would succumb to this fate believing being 'put out of misery' to be expected of them... This Bill is dangerous and threatening. Please do not feed into the deeply negative cultural response to terminal disablement by supporting it. If you do, I and many other severely disabled people will not perceive your decision as an act of compassion but one founded in fear and prejudice.

Jane was born with spinal muscular atrophy, a so-called 'terminal' condition. Her mother was told to take her home and enjoy her as she would die within a year. 'As so often with severe impairments, the doctors were wrong. I was frequently unwell, mostly with serious chest infections, but I am still here. I have spent nearly all my life desperately trying to prove that I should be alive, that I am not suffering, that I am not worthless.'[1]

Jane cannot lift her head from the pillow unaided and she needs a ventilator to help her breathe at night. She uses a powered wheelchair and has a computer on which she types with one finger. She feels fortunate to live in a borough that provides exemplary social care, in particular a twenty-four-hour personal assistant who enables Jane to have an independent life, to be a wife to her husband and a person to her family and friends.

In January 2003 Jane was hospitalised with severe pneumonia in both lungs. On two separate occasions, doctors told her they assumed that if she fell unconscious she wouldn't want to be given life-saving treatment. They explained that it would mean being on a ventilator – and she wouldn't want that, would she? She responded by asking for an article she had just had published in *The Independent* to be circulated to all the staff, entitled 'Don't be fooled, we don't all want to die'.

> I was so frightened of what might happen to me that I kept myself awake for forty-eight hours. My husband brought in a photo of me in my graduation gown and stuck it on the bed-head to remind the hospital staff that there was more to me than the shrivelled form they saw lying in front of them.[2]

Jane regards herself as lucky. Although she could barely breathe, she had an assertive husband insisting to the doctors that Jane had everything to live for. But what happens if you are unable to communicate or have relatives that are less vocal and less enthusiastic to see you leave hospital? Then consider what might happen if euthanasia was legal and the doctors and the patient's family conclude that you would be better off dead.

Reflecting upon Jane's experiences, one completely understands why disability rights groups have been united in their opposition to euthanasia and assisted suicide. Personal testimonies like Jane's and like this one from the 'Changing Perspectives' organisation that was circulated to peers before our debate on

Lord Joffe's Bill in 2003 have been extremely persuasive:

> ...When the pain is at its worst I cannot move or speak. This can go on for hours, and there is no prospect of relief... I hooded painkillers and swallowed huge overdoses, washing them down with whatever alcohol I could lay my hands on. I wanted death and knew exactly what I was doing. Fortunately for me, I have friends who were brave enough to intervene, who dialled 999 and had me rushed to hospital. I was treated against my will more than once. If euthanasia had been legal, I would have certainly requested it and I wouldn't be here now. I'll always be grateful to my friends who saved my life (though I wasn't at the time). And I'm especially thankful there was no possibility of persuading doctors to legally help me to die.

Having spoken to many disability rights campaigners it is quite clear that they are not interested in 'assisted dying' legislation. Of far greater use to them would be 'assisted living' legislation.

One of the saddest implications of the high profile media cases of Diane Pretty and Reginald Crew is that the impression has been given that as far as people with disabilities are concerned, their most sought after right is a right to an assisted death. Dr Jane Campbell wryly observes that 'The right, for example, to go to the loo when needed, which may have some cost implications and packs absolutely no emotional punch whatever is currently seen to be very much the poor relation.'

Jane readily admits that if her local authority suddenly withdrew her personal care package her life would be intolerable and she would consider suicide. This is why assistance with independent living is so important to people with disabilities and why it is so sad that local authorities are having to limit the cost of care packages – often to the lower cost of living in residential care. There are wide discrepancies in provision for disabled people with similar needs; where you live and when you joined the queue are the determining factors for the type and quality of support you receive. These inequalities must be addressed by Government as a matter of priority.

Otherwise, it is only far too easy for people with disabilities to buy into the negative stereotypes that people hold of them – as burdensome, tragic and a drain on society. Once these stereotypes take root, demands for euthanasia and assisted suicide are never far behind. Studies in

Oregon and Holland, where euthanasia is legal, revealed that a substantial number of people seeking assisted suicide gave 'not wanting to be a burden' as the principal reason for seeking death.

Speaking at a meeting in the House of Lords, Liz Sayce, Director of Policy and Communications at the Disability Rights Commission, spoke of the ease with which, 'in a culture that still views disability as a tragedy and disabled people as helpless victims, many people who become disabled assume at first that their life is over.' She cited the story of Dr Ian Basnett:

> I became quadriplegic following a sporting accident seventeen years ago. I was ventilator dependent for a while and at times said to people, 'I wish I was dead!' I am now extraordinarily glad no one acted on that and assisted suicide was not legal. I think the first difficulty I faced was the fact that, like many people, I had a terribly negative image of disability. When you suddenly become severely disabled you still have that viewpoint. Before I was disabled, I [once said] 'I'd rather be dead, if I couldn't play sport.'[3]

Liz Sayce went on to give a number of instances where assisted living had helped to ameliorate the desire for assisted dying. In one American case a man fought vigorously for the right to die – via the courts and media coverage which mentioned his major communication impairment. A software company stepped in and provided specialist equipment and others raised funds to provide him with home-based support. After that he no longer wanted to die. He had gained the dignity and independence he thought he had lost forever. He embraced life as a disabled person.

In essence it all boils down to a question of priorities. Should we not legislate to ensure that people with disabilities are given sufficient support to enable them to live with dignity and independence before we even consider legalising assisted suicide and euthanasia? In Oregon in the United States it would seem that they have already decided upon their priorities. In this State, where assisted suicide is legal, there is a State-funded 'Comfort Care' package that will fund a lethal injection (at a cost to the public purse of between $35-$45) – at the same time that the State rations pain relief and even treatment of late stage cancer for those poorer inhabitants dependent on public health services. We do not have to go down the same road here.

Those in favour of euthanasia and assisted suicide always recoil in horror when it is suggested that people with disabilities would feel more vulnerable were euthanasia and assisted suicide ever legalised. They argue that each individual's 'autonomy' would be respected, whether or not they are disabled, and that any legislation would have built in 'safeguards' to prevent vulnerable individuals from having their lives prematurely terminated. These 'safeguards' usually include the need for a terminal illness or incurable disability, for a settled wish to die and for the agreement of at least two doctors that the patient is suffering unbearably.

Yet as the disability rights campaigner Alison Davis (who has spina bifida and emphysema) points out:

> Far from 'safeguarding' anything, these requirements always in effect prescribe who is to be considered 'right to want to die' and thus be helped to die. Those who may be equally suicidal but do not have obvious disabling conditions are considered 'wrong to want to die' and are helped to live.[4]

Legalising euthanasia and assisted suicide, regardless of the safeguards that might be built in to any such legislation, would place disabled people in mortal danger. 'The campaign to assist our so-called voluntary death is dangerous and reinforces our unequal status.'[5] Disability rights groups appreciate that in a society obsessed with the 'body beautiful' and increasingly intolerant of physical and mental imperfection, the individuals they represent would go right to the front of the queue for an assisted death. Pope John Paul II has spoken of:

> ...a war of the powerful against the weak: a life which would require greater acceptance, love and care is considered useless, or held to be an intolerable burden, and is therefore rejected in one way or another. A person who, because of illness, handicap or, more simply, just by existing, compromises the wellbeing or lifestyle of those who are more favoured tends to be looked upon as an enemy to be resisted or eliminated.[6]

Disability rights groups do not seek our pity. Quite the reverse. What they do seek is a society that values the able bodied and the disabled equally and questions why it is that people like Diane Pretty view their lives as not worth living.

One of the talks that I give to sixth-form groups, parishes and university associations is entitled 'Choose Life'. This title is taken from the following beautiful passage in Deuteronomy:

> I have set before you life and death, blessings
> and curses. Now choose life, that you and
> your children may live.[7]

Practically speaking, to 'choose life' means that
we must support the efforts of disability rights
groups to tackle the under-funding and regional
disparities in personal care packages. Nor should
we leave the funding of hospices in such a
precarious state – too frequently, especially in
the case of children's hospices – entirely reliant
on voluntary endeavours.

But in addition to ensuring that resources serve
the cause of life we must also redouble our efforts
to fight eugenic abortion. As many disability
rights groups now recognise, a society which
terminates the lives of the unborn solely on the
ground of disability cannot maintain that it is
committed to valuing the lives of the able-bodied
and the disabled equally. Eugenic abortion feeds
into negative stereotypes of disability which, in
turn, fuel the campaign for euthanasia for those
whose lives are deemed not worth living. An
abortion law which authorises abortion up to
and including birth for conditions such as Down's
syndrome and cleft lip and cleft palate also fatally
undermines the claims of euthanasia advocates
that sufficient safeguards against abuse can be

built into any law that authorises the termination of life.

The vociferous opposition of disability rights groups to euthanasia can help transform the euthanasia debate from one focused on how we can help people to die to one focused on how we can help people to live. The fact that euthanasia advocates have, so far, failed to listen to such opposition betrays their libertarian 'me, my, I' agenda. We are not isolated individuals living in our own bubbles. The decisions I take and the choices I make affect others. This is why a law allowing some patients with say, Motor Neurone Disease, to request euthanasia would inevitably lead to others with the same disease asking themselves whether or not they should be making the same request. We must not place people with terminal illness and disabilities in this position.

NOTES

1 Campbell, J., *The Independent*, 'Don't Be Fooled: We Don't All Want To Kill Ourselves' (21 January 2003, p.17).

2 Dr Jane Campbell, *The Guardian*, 'Choose life: There is growing support for moves to help the severely disabled to die. But why not help them to live instead?' (26 August 2003, p.17).

3 Presentation at a meeting in the Moses Room, House of Lords 3 June 2003.

4 Davis, A., 'Briefing Notes on Voluntary Euthanasia/Assisted Dying'; July 2004;
   http://www.spuc.org.uk/euthanasia/joffe/briefing.pdf

5 Dr Jane Campbell, *The Independent*, 'Don't Be Fooled: We Don't All Want To Kill Ourselves' (21 January 2003, p.17).

6 *Evangelium Vitae* (March 1995, para. 12).

7 Chapter 30, v. 19.

Conclusion

As some political and medical opinion begins to be seduced by the arguments of the Voluntary Euthanasia Society into adopting a 'neutral' position instead of one of opposition it is worth remembering what the men and women on the ground are thinking.

Recall the poll of British doctors: 61 per cent state that they do not want euthanasia legalised – with a further 13 per cent undecided. Most doctors are so opposed – some 76 per cent – that they say that if euthanasia were legalised they would refuse to perform it. Not one single palliative care doctor who responded to the survey said they would be prepared to practise euthanasia or assisted suicide. Professor Tim Maughan, the director of Wales Cancer Trials Network at Cardiff University, put it succinctly: 'this is not what we became doctors to do.'

This debate has been manufactured by lobby groups with a clear agenda. Despite all the publicity hype around the tragic cases of Diane Pretty and Reg Crew, half the doctors who were surveyed said that in the past three years not a single patient or their relatives had requested euthanasia. More than half, 59 per cent of the doctors, said that the British Medical Association were right to resist moves to legalise euthanasia.

The Hospice Movement has warned of the dire consequences. Dr Nigel Sykes, Medical director of St Christopher's Hospice in London says 'Euthanasia without express request will inevitably follow voluntary euthanasia. Patients will be made to think that euthanasia is the decent thing to do.'

All the talk nowadays is about autonomy – and the right to do with one's life as one chooses. 'Autonomy' is one of the buzz words of the pro-euthanasia lobby. However, autonomy is not an absolute right that each of us, as individuals, can exercise while living in our own little bubbles. No-one can fail to be moved by tragic cases but the 1994 House of Lords Select Committee on Medical Ethics, chaired by Lord Walton of Detchant, was fundamentally right to argue that:

> Individual cases cannot reasonably establish the foundation of a policy (the legalisation of euthanasia) which would have such serious

and widespread repercussions. Moreover dying is not only a personal or individual affair. The death of a person affects the lives of others... We believe that the issue of euthanasia is one in which the interest of the individual cannot be separated from the interest of society as a whole.

As Britain considers adopting Dutch-style laws, on the back of these 'hard cases', be absolutely clear what has happened there. The Dutch first decriminalised their laws; then enacted voluntary euthanasia; then permitted involuntary euthanasia; and now it has become so routine that many doctors do not even bother to report it. I was in Holland when the Dutch Government officially reported that in the preceding year there were some 3,800 cases of euthanasia and that 900 – one in four – was involuntary. So much for patient autonomy.

In July 2001 the United Nations Human Rights Committee issued a report which expressed carefully worded concern over the legalisation of euthanasia in the Netherlands and its potential impact.[1] The committee report said: 'such a practice may lead to routinisation and insensitivity to the strict application of the requirements.' The Committee also expressed scepticism over the very few negative assessments made in over 2000 cases of assisted suicide and euthanasia in the Netherlands. The report states: 'The large numbers involved raise doubts whether the present system is being used in extreme cases in which all the substantive conditions are scrupulously maintained.' In addition, the UN committee noted that Dutch monitoring of euthanasia detects abuses only after the patient has been killed, and called for strengthening of mechanisms to catch violations in advance of death. The Human Rights Committee also urged a scrupulous investigation of reports that newborn infants with disabilities have had their lives ended by medical personnel. As far as I am aware, the concerns of this United Nations Committee have gone unheeded by the Dutch authorities.

So there we have it. We decriminalise; we move to voluntary euthanasia; we move on to involuntary euthanasia; and then, because it becomes so routine, we move on to non-reporting in some 50 per cent of cases. And in the course of doing this we destroy the relationship between doctors and their patients.

The revelations in early 2005 that euthanasia is being practised on babies and infants in the Netherlands, despite the fact that euthanasia is technically legal in Holland only for patients aged over twelve, should act as a salutary warning to us all.[2] Doctors at the Gröningen hospital have admitted that at least twenty-two newborn babies have been put to death since 1997 based on the doctors' own reports to public prosecutors. This information came to light in a recent report in the *Dutch Journal of Medicine*. The author of the report, Dr Eduard Verhagen, the head of the paediatrics unit at Gröningen University Hospital, said that doctors put to death between ten and fifteen infants a year.

What we need in Britain are more resources for geriatric care and for hospices, not laws encouraging the killing of patients. To die with dignity we don't need doctors to kill us. As these dangers hover before our gates I hope that this book will act as a wake-up call. The Appendix contains contact details for individuals and organisations fighting euthanasia and promoting the positive alternatives. I urge you to take action.

NOTES

1 United Nations Human Rights Committee 72nd Session, 27 July 2001;
   http://www.unhchr.ch/huricane/huricane.nsf/NewsRoom?OpenFrameSet
2 *The Daily Telegraph* (Monday, 24 January 2005).

APPENDIX

If you would like to help promote a culture of life in this country and beyond but need more information about how, when and where to act, please contact at least one of the following individuals and/or organisations. They will be happy to help.

- Jim Dobbin MP, Chairman
  All-Party Parliamentary Pro-life Group
  House of Commons
  London
  SW1A 0AA
  Tel: 020 7219 4530
  Fax: 020 7219 2696
  Email: dobbinj@parliament.uk
  Web: www.parliamentaryprolife.org.uk

- Martin Foley, Chief Executive
  LIFE
  Newbold Terrace
  Leamington Spa
  Warwickshire
  CV32 4EA
  Tel: 01926 311667
  Fax: 01926 336497
  Email: info@lifeuk.org
  Web: www.lifeuk.org

- Phyllis Bowman, Director
  Right to Life
  PO Box 26264
  London
  W3 9WF
  Tel: 020 8992 7657
  Fax: 020 8896 1859
  Email: Phyllis@righttolife.org.uk
  Web: www.righttolife.org.uk

- Josephine Quintavalle, Director
  Comment on Reproductive Ethics (CORE)
  PO Box 4593
  London
  SW3 6XE
  Tel: 020 7581 2623
  Fax: 020 7581 3868
  Email: info@corethics.org
  Web: www.corethics.org

- Julia Millington
  ProLife Alliance
  PO Box 13395
  London
  SW3 6XE
  Tel: 020 7581 6939
  Fax: 020 7581 3868
  Email: info@prolife.org.uk
  Web: www.prolife.org.uk

- Roger Smith, Head of Public Policy
  Christian Action, Research and Education (CARE)
  53 Romney Street
  London
  SW1P 3RF
  Tel: 020 7233 0455
  Fax: 020 7233 0983
  Email: mail@care.org.uk
  Web: www.care.org.uk

- Peter Saunders, General Secretary
  Christian Medical Fellowship
  Partnership House
  157 Waterloo Road
  London
  SE1 8XN
  Tel: 020 7928 4694
  Fax: 020 7620 2453
  Email: pjs@cmf.org.uk
  Web: www.cmf.org.uk

- Andrea Minichiello Williams,
  Public Policy Officer
  Lawyers' Christian Fellowship
  4 Lucas Grange
  Haywards Heath, West Sussex
  RH16 1JS
  Tel: 0771 2591164
  Email: andrea@williamsa.force9.co.uk
  Web: www.lawcf.org

Abortion

Getting to the heart of the matter
by David Alton with Martin Foley

Since the passing of the Abortion Act in 1967 in the UK (with the exception of Northern Ireland) there have been six million abortions. Even more shocking, the number of abortions in the UK is rising year-on-year and the age of women seeking abortions is getting younger. Pragmatism about abortion and a growing disregard for the sanctity of human life have permeated society to its core – abortion is seen as just another form of birth control.

This readable and up-to-the-minute booklet informs readers of the latest research on abortion – abortion and disability; abortion and its psychological and physical effect on womens' health, particularly its link with breast cancer; the promotion of chemical abortions; and the stories of inspiring women such as Norma McCorvey. It will help individuals and groups understand how to influence public policy and how best to aid those most at risk. A useful list of names and addresses is included in the Appendix.

ISBN 085439 691 8   96pp

ALSO BY DAVID ALTON

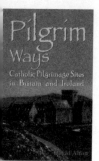

Pilgrim Ways

Catholic Pilgrimage Sites in Britain and Ireland

This guide provides the history, spiritual inspiration and practical information to enhance any pilgrimage – a blend of fascinating facts and personal experience. The author takes us on a journey from great cathedrals and holy wells, to Marian shrines and monasteries; from Croagh Patrick and Knock to the Tower of London. As well as covering many well known pilgrimage sites, he also gives a suggestion for a 'walk of witness' from Westminster Cathedral to Tyburn Convent in London, taking in some fascinating churches on the way.

'We each set out to visit holy places for different reasons. PILGRIM WAYS reminds us that, whatever the purpose, each pilgrimage is an opportunity for us to turn from what separates us from God and to discover new insight into the perfect love that he has for each one of us.'

Cardinal Cormac Murphy-O'Connor

ISBN 085439 605 5   335pp   £11.95